Dedication

To the inmates of Bedford Hills Correctional Facility
Bedford Hills, New York

It is my prayer that you will find the
only real freedom there is,
the freedom I have found in Jesus Christ.

Chapter I

The Abortion

"I saw the doctor today, Frank," I said, "and I'm pregnant."

Frank gave me a startled look. Then without hesitation he said, "You can have an abortion in Cuba. Abortions are legal in Cuba."

"Abortion!" I cried. "Frank, we could get married and have the baby."

"You seem to forget I *am* married," he said.

"If you told Dolores about the baby, she might give you a divorce."

"If she hasn't divorced me by now," he said, "I don't know when she will."

I'd been so sure he'd push for a divorce.

"Then you can divorce her," I said.

He gave a short, bitter laugh. "I'm supporting one child already."

"For three years you've promised me you'd get a divorce and we'd be married." I couldn't hold back the tears any longer. "I never would have moved in with you if I thought this was going to happen."

"You've got to be practical, Celeste, and deal with this problem right now," Frank said. "Tomorrow you'll take a plane to Cuba. There are spotters at the airport, men who take girls to abortion doctors."

"What if something goes wrong?" I cried. I'd heard terrible stories about women dying from abortions.

"Nothing will go wrong," he said. "Thousands of women have abortions."

I could tell by his face that there was no point in discussing it further.

The next morning I dressed quickly and quietly. I didn't want to wake Frank. He had told me the night before to call a cab. As I left the bedroom I glanced at him. He was sound asleep, completely oblivious to my fear and loneliness.

Twenty minutes later I was at the airport. As I boarded the plane, tears blurred my vision. It wasn't that I wanted the baby, but I had been so sure that Frank and I would be married. I wondered now if we would ever be married.

I sat down next to an attractive girl.

"I'm Constance Bianco," she said. "I've been visiting my parents in New York, but I live in Cuba with my boyfriend, Mario."

"I'm Celeste Clemente," I said. "I live in New York with my boyfriend, and I'm going to Cuba to have an abortion. I'm going to go with one of those spotters at the airport."

"Oh, don't do that," she said. "Don't go off with one of those spotters. You don't know what kind of butcher you'll end up with. Mario's father, Dominic, will be able to help you."

"How can he help me?" I asked.

"Dominic is a very big man in the Mafia," she said.

She wrote a name and telephone number on a piece of paper for me. Then I wrote my name and the name of my hotel on a piece of paper and gave it to Constance.

"As soon as I get to my apartment," she said, "I'll tell Dominic about you. Then you can call him."

An hour after I checked into my hotel, I called Dominic

Lucero and introduced myself.

"Yes, Celeste, I'm so glad you called," he said. "I hear you're a very beautiful girl. Constance says you need help."

"That's right," I said. "I'm looking for a doctor."

"I have just the right doctor for you," he said. "If you will take a cab to my apartment, I will be happy to make the necessary arrangements."

I took down his address and hung up.

I changed into a low-cut pink cotton dress and high heels.

Twenty minutes later I was in Dominic's apartment. The living room was luxurious with thick white carpeting, gilt-edged chairs, marble tables, and a large chandelier.

"I've never seen anything so beautiful!" I said.

Dominic was pleased. He was a powerfully built, good looking man in his fifties with wavy white hair and large, dark eyes.

"Celeste, you are a knockout!" he said. Then smiling, he said, "We'll have a drink."

I sat next to him on the gold brocaded couch and he pressed a buzzer under the coffee table. Immediately a teenaged boy appeared.

"Yes, Senor Lucero!" the boy said.

"Ted, bring me a pitcher of martinis."

The boy left and when I looked back at Dominic, he was eyeing me in a way I didn't like.

"Celeste, I have never seen such a voluptuous girl!"

What had I gotten myself into I wondered. Ted returned with the pitcher of martinis and two glasses. Dominic poured the cocktails and held his glass toward mine.

"Here's to us, Celeste!"

To us? Did this old man really think I could be interested in him?

"I own two casinos in Cuba," Dominic said. "All the big time racketeers from New York come down here and gamble in my places. If you like, we could play a little roulette tonight."

"No, thank you," I said. "I didn't come down here to enjoy myself."

"Celeste, you are a very sexy girl," he said. "You could make big money down here."

"I just want to make an appointment with a doctor," I said.

He laughed softly. "Celeste, you intrigue me. We have been together for almost half an hour and you haven't asked me for any money."

I stood up. "I just want to have an abortion and get back to my boyfriend," I said.

Dominic stood up. "There's no harm in having a little fun first, is there?"

"I'm going back to my hotel," I said.

"You're not going anywhere," he said evenly. "You're coming to bed with me."

"I am not!" I cried.

He took a step toward me and with one blow knocked me to the floor. Before I could get up, he began kicking me in the stomach. I screamed as the pain shot through me. The house boy came running into the room.

"Senor Lucero, stop it!" he cried.

Dominic was now kicking me in the chest.

"Senor Lucero, please don't kill her!" Ted cried. "I will get you another girl."

Dominic turned for an instant toward the boy. "Get out!" he shouted. "No woman says no to Lucero! No woman!"

As the boy fled I caught a glimpse of Dominic's face and his expression frightened me more than his kicking. He was half crazed with rage. I realized the only way I was going to stay alive was to go to bed with him.

"All right," I said. "I'll go with you."

I thought the worst was over, but when we were in bed, Dominic raped me. I was terrified, but I knew if I objected he would kill me. An hour later Dominic led me into the living room. He mixed Scotch and sodas and handed one to me.

"Celeste, if you will live with me, you may have this apartment. I will buy you beautiful clothes, jewels, a Cadillac—anything you want."

"I'll have to think about it," I said pleasantly. My mind was racing, trying to devise a way of escape.

"Would you like to accompany me to my son's apartment? he asked. "We could have dinner with Mario and Constance."

"That would be nice," I said. Maybe I could break away from him on the way.

Breaking away from Dominic, however, proved to be impossible.

When we were at Mario's apartment, Constance said, "I'm so glad we met on that plane, Celeste."

She had no idea what was going on. "So am I," I said.

Mario was a smaller version of his father. "I hope you will be in Cuba for a while," he said.

During dinner I kept up my end of the light conversation. When the meal was over, Mario stood up.

"Constance and I are going to the club," he said.

My heart sank.

"I'll be in touch with you, Celeste," Constance said and they were gone.

Dominic smiled at me. "Celeste, take a nap with me," he said.

I followed him into the bedroom. He stretched out on the bed and closed his eyes. I lay down beside him and within minutes he was snoring. I waited a couple of more minutes to be absolutely sure he was asleep. Then quietly I left the room and went out the door. To play it safe, I took the stairs and raced down twenty-one flights.

Outside I flagged a cab and returned to my hotel. When I was in my room I locked the door and pushed a heavy chair against it. Then I dialed the switchboard operator.

"This is Celeste Clemente, room 818," I said. "I will not accept any telephone calls unless they're from New York."

I took a shower and saw red welts across my body and a swelling on the left side of my abdomen. Then I put on a robe. It was such a relief to be safe, such a relief to be away from Dominic that I collapsed on the bed, sobbing.

How could this have happened to me? In the three years I'd lived with Frank, he'd never beaten me this brutally. I remembered how Frank and I had started out with so much love, so much hope. I remembered the night we met, the night Frank walked into the dance studio and I was assigned as his instructor. He was so handsome with those sparkling hazel eyes and that dazzling smile.

"Chiquita, you are very beautiful!" he said, taking my hand and kissing it.

After the dancing lesson we went out for a drink and his Latin charm and beautiful eyes had me absolutely spellbound. When he drove me home that night he said, "Carino mio, can I tell you a little secret? We are going to fall in love!" After three dates I knew I'd met the man of my dreams. Every night I met him in the restaurant where he worked as Maitre D'. For the next two months we were together almost every night.

"Carino mio, we are going to have a wonderful life together," Frank whispered. "You are my heart, my very breath!"

Later, when Frank told me he had a wife and child, it didn't matter.

"She will divorce me, Chiquita. It is simply a matter of time. Dolores is a beautiful girl and will one day remarry. Then we can be married."

One night he said, "No puedo vivir sin ti."

I loved to hear him speak in Spanish. "What does that

mean?" I asked.

"It means I can't live without you," he said. "Celeste, I must have you for my own, forever!"

"I want to spend the rest of my life loving you, Frank," I said.

"Then it's settled," he said. "I want you to live with me until we can be married."

lIn that moment everything I'd learned as a kid in church came rushing back into my heart.

"Frank, I don't think I could do that," I said.

But the following night when we were together he said, "Celeste, look at it this way. We are going to be married one day anyhow, so it really doesn't make any difference if we live together."

The next day I told Mother I was taking an apartment in the city because I was tired of commuting to work.

"You're my baby! What will I do without you?" she cried.

"Mother, you know I'll visit you," I said.

"And what will Grandma do? You are her whole life, Celeste!"

Before I moved out the following night, Grandma came over to say good bye.

"I'm not worried about you, Celeste," she said. "I pray for you three times a day and Jesus has assured me that you will come back to Him."

I couldn't wait for Grandma to leave. I felt so guilty in her presence after all the years I'd gone to the little Pentecostal church with her. When I left, Mother had tears in her eyes. Dad was sitting in his armchair with the bottle open on the end table, stoned as always. I was glad to be leaving. I was glad to be getting away from nineteen years of my father beating my mother, nineteen years of my father punching me and my sisters.

That first year with Frank was beautiful. He never tired of telling me how much he loved me. "Yo te adoro," he whispered night after night. I would have laid down my life for him. Once in a while before falling asleep I felt guilty and prayed. "Oh, God," I said, "I have to live with Frank. Please don't let me die and go to hell. Some day I'll serve you, I promise." Then one night, instead of coming home at 2 a.m., the usual time after the restaurant closed, Frank came in at 4 a.m.

"Where have you been?" I cried.

"You don't question me!" he said.

"I want to know where you've been!" I said.

Frank slapped me across the face and when I ran to the bedroom crying, he beat me. I screamed as the blows continued to fall all over my body. Finally he stopped and left the room. I sobbed until I was weak with exhaustion. A half hour later Frank was back. He put his arms around me. "Carino mio, forgive me. I want to make love to you."

I couldn't understand how he could beat me and then want to make love, but it didn't matter. I loved him so much I went along with the idea. The next day there was a bouquet of roses with a white card. "I will always love you, Frank." I would always love him too. Nothing could change that.

After that night it was as though a dam had burst. Beatings became a regular part of my life. Every couple of months Frank took out another girl and if I complained or questioned him, he beat me. I loved him so much nothing could make me leave him. What had happened to our first love, I wondered. What had become of the Frank I used to know—so tender and gentle and thoughtful?

A sudden, sharp knock on the door brought me back to the present.

"Open up, Celeste!" It was Dominic.

I lay on the bed, my heart pounding. Now he was kicking the door. I remembered the half crazed expression on his face when he had kicked me.

"If you don't open up, you are going to be one sorry girl!" he said.

If he made enough noise someone else would hear him and complain. As the door continued to rattle and shake I prayed.

"Oh, God, if You get me through this night," I said, "I promise You I'll leave Frank. I won't have the abortion. I'll go back to church!"

Suddenly there was silence. I got off the bed and went over to the window. Dominic could pay someone to climb the fire escape and cut out a pane of glass. I went back to bed. The silence continued. Dominic must have left. Every time I started to fall asleep, I awoke with my heart pounding. Finally I fell into a deep sleep, only to awake from a crashing noise against the door.

"Celeste, you might as well open up," Dominic said. "If you don't I'll wait until you come out. I don't care how many days it takes!"

I glanced at my watch. It was 4 a.m. I vowed if I lived through the night I would go back to New York in the morning. I would forget about having the abortion. I'd have the baby and Frank could do whatever he wanted. I didn't care. I had to stay alive. Dominic stopped pounding on the door and I lay very still. As the sun started to come up, I fell asleep again.

When I next awoke it was 11 a.m. I was hungry and wanted some strong coffee, but I wouldn't call room service because if Dominic was still in the hotel, he would come in with the bus boy. I wondered how I would get out of the hotel and to the airport safely. I decided to call the American Consul's office. Sitting on the edge of the bed, I picked up the receiver and placed the call.

When a man answered the phone I said, "This is Celeste Clemente. I am an American visiting in Cuba. I need your help."

"Miss, don't you read the newspapers?" The man's voice was incredulous. "The American Consul was closed yesterday. Castro has taken over the government."

I never read the newspapers and as the man tried to explain what was happening, I interrupted him.

"This is an emergency," I said. "My life is in danger!"

"Now calm down, Miss," he said. "Everyone is having an emergency."

I told him that I'd been raped and that Dominic was waiting for me.

"I wish I could help you, but we are in the midst of a bloody takeover," he said.

"Maybe the police can help me," I said.

"Miss, there are no police to respond to your call. The country is in chaos. The guerillas are in control of the government."

"What am I going to do?" I cried.

He asked for my name and address and the flight number of my plane from New York. Then he said, "When you were arriving in Cuba, the Castro guerillas were shooting at the Batista plane. Yours was one of the last tourist flights to land."

"I've got to get back to New York," I said, "but I can't leave this hotel by myself."

"I don't know when you can get back to the States," he said. "Americans are standing in line at the airport, waiting for flights."

I hung up. I wouldn't think of leaving now. If I wasn't killed by Dominic or one of his men, I'd be killed by Castro's guerillas.

I lay back on the bed, sobbing. How had I ever reached this point in my life? Maybe God was punishing me for living with Frank. "Oh, God, let me see my mother just one more time!" I cried. If Mother ever knew why I was in Cuba, she'd die. Although I never admitted it, she knew I was living with Frank. Many times when she called, Frank answered the phone. She didn't believe me when I said he was visiting. I felt so sorry for Mother. She'd had a terrible life. For thirty years she'd been beaten by my father. My brother and three sisters were long since married and gone. Mother had no one now except Grandma across the street. If Grandma knew I was contemplating an abortion, she would be horrified. Grandma was the essence of goodness and holiness. I'd spent half my childhood in her house, partly to keep away from my father and partly because I loved Grandma so much. My mind went back to the days when I was a little girl, when I would go to her house every afternoon and she would tell me a story. Of all the stories she told me, the one about Shadrach, Meshach and Abednego was my favorite.

Grandma's voice came back to me. "Once there was a bad king," she said, "King Nebuchadnezzer, who served false gods and made an image of gold. He commanded all the people in his kingdom to worship the golden image. Now there were three good men. Shadrach, Meshach and Abednego, who worshipped the one and only true God. They refused to worship the golden image and this made the king very angry. He told them that if they would not worship the golden image, he would cast them into a burning, fiery furnace.

"Shadrach, Meshach and Abednego said to the king, 'Our God whom we serve is able to deliver us from the burning, fiery furnace!' When they said that, the king was furious and called the mighty men of his kingdom together and ordered some army men to tie up Shadrach, Meshach and Abednego. Then the king told his men to make the furnace seven times hotter than usual and ordered them to throw the three good men into the burning fiery furnace. The fire was so hot that when the men threw Shadrach, Meshach and Abednego into the furnace, flames shot out and killed the army men! Then looking into the furnace, King Nebuchadnezzer was amazed and said to his mighty men, 'Did we not cast three men bound into the fire?' The men said, 'Yes, oh, king!' Then the king said, 'I see four men loose, walking in the midst of the fire, and they are not hurt; and the fourth one looks like the Son of God!' Then the king came near the door of the furnace and said, 'Shadrach, Meshach and Abednego, servants of the most high God, come forth!' The three good men, who had refused to worship the golden image, came out of the furnace and all the people saw that the fire had not burned them. Not a hair on their heads had been singed. Not even the smell of fire was on them. And King Nebuchadnezzer said, 'Blessed be the God of Shadrach, Meshach and Abednego!' "

I clapped my hands together. "Oh, Grandma, I will never worship a golden image, only the one, true God!" I cried.

"The fourth man in the furnace was Jesus!" Grandma said. "Remember, Celeste, no matter what happens in life, Jesus will always be with you. He will never leave you nor forsake you."

Those words mocked me now. I sat up on the bed and wiped the tears from my face. If Grandma knew how I'd strayed since those days, it would break her heart.

It was almost one o'clock. I decided to phone Mother.

"When are you coming out to see me?" she asked.

"Mother, I am in Cuba on a vacation," I said. "If you've heard the news, you know Castro has taken over the government down here. Everything is chaos and confusion. I don't know when or if I can get a plane back to New York."

"My god!" she cried. "Celeste, you could be killed!"

"Mother, please, every minute is important. I want you to call Frank at the restaurant and tell him to get me out of this place. He'll know what to do."

"All right," she said. "I'll keep calling until I get him. Now, don't leave your room. Don't go outside for any reason."

"Mother, I can promise you that I will not leave this room until Frank gets here."

I gave her the name and address of the hotel and hung up.

The pains in my ribs and abdomen were getting worse and I longed for a drink. I wondered if Frank would be able to land in Cuba. And if he did, would we be able to take a flight back to New York. I wondered where Dominic was and when he would be back. With no police available, Dominic would be able to get away with anything. If Frank came down I wouldn't have to worry about Dominic. If I had a man with me, Dominic wouldn't come near me.

Early the following afternoon there was a knock on my door. I held my breath. The knocking grew louder.

"Chiquita, it's me. Frank!"

I opened the door and fell against him, crying weakly. Frank led me to the large upholstered chair and cradled me in his arms. I told him what Dominic had done to me.

"Carino Mio," he said. "What a terrible thing has happened to my little one!"

He kept stroking my hair and kissing my cheek. Later, he called room service and ordered dinner.

"Celeste, we can't waste any time," he said. "Because of this take over of the government, we have to get out of here as quickly as possible. We'll have to find a doctor this afternoon and then go right back to New York."

After dinner we went downstairs and the maitre d' gave Frank the name and address of an abortionist. We took a cab to the doctor's office.

When it was my turn to be seen, Frank stood up. "I'll be back in an hour," he said. "Don't worry about anything."

I signed over my traveler's checks to the doctor and the nurse took me into the examining room. I changed into a white gown and the doctor came in.

"Get up on the table, please," he said.

He put a needle in my arm and the nurse said, "You

will feel drowsy."

"How did you get all these contusions?" the doctor asked.

"Someone kicked me," I said.

A minute later I relaxed a little, but I was not the least bit drowsy. Suddenly I felt an instrument high up inside of me. The pain was excruciating and I screamed.

"If you scream again, I will stop the abortion," the doctor said.

He continued cutting and the pain seared through me. I shrieked.

"God damn it! Stop moving!" he said. "Why didn't you scream when you were making this baby?"

I bit my lip until it bled. The nurse placed a pillow over my face and said, "Bite the pillow."

Soon there were feathers in my mouth. I was sure I was going to die. Silently I screamed, "Oh, God, please don't let me die and go to hell!"

In the next minute the abortion was over with and the nurse wheeled me into another room.

Chapter II

The Golden Image

After the abortion things were never the same again. When Frank beat me, there were no flowers the next day. As time went by the affairs with other girls became more frequent. The hours he spent away from me, I now accepted.

Frank and I had been living together almost four years when I became friends with Lynn, a barmaid in a lounge where Frank and I went for a nightcap when he took me out on Monday nights. Lynn lived only a few blocks from our apartment and I began visiting her on Saturdays. She was living with her boyfriend, Ernie, and he treated her well. When I told them about the beatings from Frank, they were both shocked.

"Celeste, you're a beautiful girl," Ernie said. "You don't have to take that!"

"You could get any man you want," Lynn said, "so why do you put up with it?"

"I don't want any man but Frank," I said.

I couldn't make them understand.

Then late one night when Frank and I were asleep the doorbell rang. I wrapped a towel around myself and opened the door. A young couple was standing there.

The girl, a beautiful redhead, said, "We'd like to see Frank."

"Who are you?" I asked.

"I'm Inez," she said. "We want to talk to Frank."

I assumed the man was her husband or her boyfriend and I went to the bedroom and called Frank.

When he came into the living room and saw them standing in the doorway, his eyes hardened.

"You should not have come here!" he said.

"What do you mean, I should not have come here!" Inez cried. "I'm pregnant and you're the father!"

"Get the hell out of here!" Frank shouted.

"I'm her brother," the man said, "and I mean to see that you do the right thing by her."

Frank slammed the door and locked it.

I was speechless. Then my heart started pounding and I cried out, "Is that true, Frank? Did you get that girl pregnant?"

He slapped me across the face.

"How long have you been seeing her?" I screamed. "How long do you think I am going to put up with this?"

He slapped me again and this time I staggered and fell on the floor. Frank picked me up, carried me into the bedroom and dropped me on the bed. His fists came down in the hollow of my back and I screamed. He went into a frenzy and beat me until I thought I'd pass out. When it was over and he left the room, I quickly put on my clothes, grabbed my coat and bag and ran from the apartment. I got into my car and drove to Lynn's apartment. Ernie opened the door.

"My God, Celeste, what happened to you?" he asked.

I walked past him and fell on the couch, hysterical. Lynn came running from the bedroom. Ernie gave me a double Scotch.

"You have got to leave that guy!" he said.

Lynn put her arm around me. "Celeste, you'll sleep here tonight," she said, "but tomorrow you must start looking for your own apartment."

The next day I was in such pain, I couldn't go to the dance studio. I told Lynn what Inez had said and she was outraged.

"Celeste, you're crazy to stay with him!" she said.

I could not make her understand that in spite of the unfaithfulness, in spite of the beatings, I still loved Frank.

Late that afternoon I went back to our apartment. Exhausted and depressed, I lay on the bed. Lynn and Ernie were right. All their arguments made sense. I should leave Frank, but I loved him. I couldn't live without him. Great sobs shook my body. Why couldn't Frank love me the way he used to? Why were the beatings getting more frequent and more severe? As I looked back over the years I realized my whole life had revolved around beatings. As far back as I could remember, my father had beaten my mother, night after night. When I was very small and heard Mother scream, I ran to her begging her to get away from Dad. And then I was punched by my father. Screaming in terror, I fell to the floor with blood spurting from my nose. Sometimes my brother Chris picked me up and ran from the house. My sisters kept out of sight during the beatings. As I grew older, instead of trying to help Mother, I hid or ran out of the house. And yet, as a small child, I loved my father. He took me to Mass every Sunday, just the two of us. I was his favorite. Then later at home he played with me, swinging me around and laughing. "My bambino! My bambino!" he cried and he kissed me over and over again. He put me on top of a ladder so I could see him cut the hedge in the front yard. Later I followed him around the back yard as he cleaned out the chicken coop and the goat pen. I liked to watch him milk the nanny goat. But soon the beatings and screaming made up most of my life and I began to hate my father. When I walked home from school, I never knew if I would find my mother injured. My biggest fear was that I would find Mother dead. The afternoons that I saw Dad swaying down the street, I ran to Grandmother's house. Grandma was always happy, always singing hymns to the Lord. I spent more time with her and began going to the little Pentecostal church with her. At the end of each service Pastor Wilcox said, "Let's tarry for the Holy Ghost." I got to see things most kids never saw because their families had to go home early.

One night as Mrs. Wilcox played the organ the people sang a hymn that was to become my favorite. "There's room at the cross for you. There's room at the cross for you. Though millions have come, there's still room for one. There's room at the cross for you." The pastor laid his hands on a young man's head and prayed. Suddenly the young man began to speak in a language I didn't understand.

"Jesus baptized him with the Holy Ghost," Grandma said. "He's speaking in tongues, a heavenly language only God can understand."

Then the pastor went over to an old woman and laid his hands on her head; as he prayed in tongues, the woman fell like a leaf to the floor.

"She's all right," Grandma said. "She is slain under the Spirit of God. You can't stand when the power hits you."

At one service Pastor Wilcox preached on salvation. He opened the Bible and read, "For by grace are ye saved through faith; and that not of yourselves: it is the gift of God: Not of works, lest any man should boast." Pastor closed the Bible. "You cannot get to heaven by keeping the commandments and doing good deeds," he said. "The only way you can get to heaven is to accept the gift of salvation. When Jesus died on the cross, He paid the penalty for your sins and all you have to do is accept Jesus."

The more I heard about Jesus, the more I loved Him.

"Is there anyone here tonight, who needs Jesus?" the pastor asked.

I walked up to the altar. "I want Jesus," I said.

Pastor put his hands on my head and said, "Celeste, repeat this prayer after me."

I raised my arms toward heaven and repeated his words: "Jesus, I acknowledge You as my Savior and I repent of my sins. I ask You to come into my heart and I make You Lord of my life!"

As I spoke those words I was overwhelmed with love and later, going home from church with Grandma, I could still feel that love all through me.

"Celeste, you will never be the same little girl again," Grandma said. "You are now a child of God and no one will be able to pluck you out of His hand."

I sat up in bed. "Oh, God, whatever happened to those days?" I cried. How could I have lost all that love and peace and joy? I got off the bed and took a shower. Then I put on a gold satin dress I knew Frank liked and brushed my hair. He would be home around 2 a.m. I decided not to mention anything about Inez again. Frank and I would make up and I would settle for what little happiness he could give me.

When he came in later, he took me in his arms. "Mi amor," he whispered. "I still love you."

I put my arms around him, happy and grateful to have his love again. My life continued in the same old way— making love one night, being beaten the next. Then about a month later, one night around 1 a.m. the telephone rang. When I picked up the receiver and said, "Hello," a girl's voice said, "This is Monica. I'm calling to tell you that Frank is in love with me and you'd better give him up."

"Frank is in love with me!" I cried. "And I will never give him up!"

"If you don't give him up," she said. "I'll kill myself."

By the time Frank came home at 4 a.m., I'd had several drinks and was pacing the floor.

When I repeated the telephone conversation to him, he said, "She won't kill herself."

"Then it's true!" I screamed. "You've been seeing her. You're in love with her!"

"Celeste, believe me, I am not in love with her," he said.

"Then where were you until 4 a.m.?" I demanded.

"You don't question me," he said and before I could duck, he punched me in the mouth. I fell on the couch, sobbing and he beat me until I was too weak to cry any more. When he went to the bedroom I put on my coat, took my bag, and drove to Lynn's.

It was pointless to discuss the situation with Lynn and Ernie but I needed their friendship and I needed a place to stay for one night.

The next afternoon I broke down and told Lynn about Monica. As I was leaving her apartment, Lynn said, "Celeste, where is your self-respect?"

I couldn't answer her. I'd never thought of that before.

Back in our apartment I waited up all night for Frank, but for the first time he failed to come home. The following afternoon I called the restaurant and asked to speak to him.

"Don't you ever call me at work again," he said. "And don't come in here." He hung up.

Frank did not come home that night or the next night. My worst fear had always been that I would lose him to another woman. And now, finally, I was sure it had happened. I became hysterical. "Oh, God, why did You ever let me meet Frank in the first place?" I cried. I was better off when I was living at home. With all the bedlam, at least I'd had my mother's love. At least I'd had Grandma. I longed for the days when Grandma and I went to the little Pentecostal church together. I remembered the time we went to revival. I was only seven years old, but I would never forget that night. Sister Veronica, a missionary who worked in India, stood at the altar and told us about her mission field.

"The people in India do not have enough food and many of them die of starvation," she said. "It is a terrible thing to die without knowing Jesus. In my village many Indians have given their hearts to Jesus, but there are thousands of poor people dying without knowing Jesus. We don't have enough missionaries to tell them about the Lord."

I felt so sorry for the people who didn't know Jesus. I wanted everyone in the world to know Him.

"Is there anyone in this church who would like to be a missionary and win lost souls for Jesus?" she asked.

I raised my hand and she called me up to the altar. Then she asked my name and laid her hands upon my head and began to pray in tongues. Suddenly her voice rang out. "Celeste, you have been ordained by God to go forth and preach the gospel! Some day you will become a missionary for the Lord Jesus!"

A tremendous love filled my heart and I raised my arms and cried out, "Lord, I will serve you all the days of my life!"

During the years that followed I visualized myself working as a missionary in a mud hut, ministering to the sick and telling them how much Jesus loved them.

As I grew up, my family became smaller. First Chris went in the Army, then Marilyn, my oldest sister, eloped. Two years later Vera eloped and that left only Rita and me. When I was thirteen, Rita was married. Soon I began to hate my life and couldn't wait until I was old enough to move out of the house. When I was fourteen I became hypnotized by movies and soap operas on TV, and for the first time I had hope. If I grew up to be beautiful, I would find Prince Charming and live happily ever after.

He would take me away from my father's drunken rages and out of a lifetime of poverty. Within the next year my figure developed and my life changed completely. The boys were crazy about me and I started going out with the fast crowd. Staying out late drinking became a way of life. Little by little I stopped going to church. When I was sixteen, one night Grandma said to me, "Celeste, I'm not worried about you. God is married to the backslider and some day you will come back to Jesus!"

How wrong Grandma had been! I would never go back to Jesus. It was too late for that. My life hadn't worked out. Jesus was a part of my childhood, and like my childhood, He was gone forever.

Frank came back at the end of a week, contrite and loving.

"Celeste, the day after Monica called you, I got a call at work. She tried to kill herself."

"Well, obviously she didn't succeed," I said.

"She cut her wrists a little," he said. "I had to stay with her until she calmed down. Celeste, you have to believe me. I am not going back to her."

He pulled me against him. "Mi cielo, I am sorry. Forgive me," he said.

I put my arms around him. All I knew was that I loved him and I would love him forever. We slipped back into our old pattern and as the weeks and months went by, I felt more and more sorry for myself. I began to resent all the hours I had to spend alone. I began to resent Frank's selfishness. Except for his day off, he never took me out. He never bought me a gift and he never gave me any money, although he always had plenty to spend on himself.

For the past couple of months Frank had been coming home very late two and three nights a week. I didn't say anything because I couldn't take any more beatings. And besides, he would become tired of this girl just as he had with all the others. But a third month went by and I felt a new fear. This was the first time he had gone out for more than two months with the same girl. Then one Saturday night as I was waiting up for him, I was startled when he burst through the door. He was furious.

"Celeste, I want you out of this apartment!" he shouted.

I braced myself. Whatever was coming, I would live through it. "What's the matter?" I asked.

His clear hazel eyes held mine for a moment. Then suddenly the anger left his face. "All right, I'll tell you," he said. "It's better to be honest."

He sat down on the chair opposite me. "I've met a girl I want to marry," he said.

"Marry?" I cried. He'd never marry anyone. With Frank it was just one girl after the other. He didn't want any responsibility.

"I'm serious, Celeste. I have met a girl who is different from all the others."

"What could be so different?"

"Of all the girls I've met, Roberta is the first one who won't go to bed with me. She said, 'If you want to go to bed with me, you'll have to marry me.'"

"You'd marry her just to go to bed with her?"

"I'm in love with her," Frank said.

"Oh, Frank, you've been in love a hundred times," I said.

"Roberta is different," he said. "She is from Ecuador and works as a Flamingo dancer. She's only eighteen years old and her aunt goes everywhere with her as a chaperone. She isn't allowed out on a date without her aunt."

"You would never marry anyone," I said. "Besides, Dolores will never give you a divorce."

"I divorced Dolores two weeks ago," he said.

"What?" I screamed. "I don't believe it!"

"Roberta and I are going to be married next Saturday," he said.

"I won't let you get married!" I cried.

"You can't stop me," he said evenly.

"I'll never give you up. Never!"

I could not believe that this was any different from all the other affairs.

Frank stood up. "I want you out now," he said. "I am not asking you, I am telling you!"

He took a step toward me, but before he could hit me I ran to the phone and dialed the operator and told her to send the police. I was not going to take one more beating. Frank went into the bedroom and closed the door. Two minutes later the doorbell rang.

I opened the door and two cops were standing there. I asked them in and Frank came out of the bedroom. He looked at me very calmly, almost smugly.

"I want you to make this man leave the apartment," I said to the cops.

"She's got it backwards, officer," Frank said. "She's the one who has to leave. This is my apartment." Then he took a document from his pocket and handed it to the cop. "Here's my lease," he said.

The cop read through it quickly, then looked at me. "Miss, you'll have to leave," he said. "This is his apartment and he has the right to ask you to leave."

The cops left and when I looked at Frank, his eyes were smouldering. "Now get out!" he said.

I could not believe what was happening to me. I ran to the kitchen, sobbing. I wanted a glass of water. Suddenly I heard a scraping sound behind me and I turned. Frank had a wrought iron chair in his hand and was coming at me. I turned away to protect my face and as I did, he smashed the chair over my back and I fell to the floor, pain exploding through my body. I cried out and the pain became unbearable. I got up and went into the bedroom. I took my coat and bag and left.

As I walked to my car I could hardly breathe with the pain. I didn't remember driving home. When Mother opened the door she cried out, "My God, what happened to you, Celeste?"

"Take me to the hospital, Mother," I said quietly.

After the X-rays were taken I lay on the examining table in the emergency room. A doctor was standing over me.

"You're a very lucky girl," he said. "You've got a hairline fracture of the spine. With rest it will heal in a few weeks."

He put a needle in my arm. "This will ease the pain," he said.

I was hardly aware of the doctor or what he said. It didn't matter what he had found in the X-rays. The only thing that mattered was that it was all over between Frank and me. I'd loved Frank with all of my heart. Never once had I been unfaithful to him. I was twenty-four years old and I'd wasted five precious years of my life. What a fool I'd been. Finally, I was tired of being used. Finally, I was tired of being beaten. Never again would I trust a man. I had a new god now—money. I was going to get all the money I could get. And I didn't care how I got it. I was going to the top. And I didn't care how I got there. In that emergency room I sold my soul to the devil.

Chapter III

A Taste of Money

I went to Mother's house to recuperate and the following day my sister Rita drove to Frank's apartment and brought back all my belongings.

When my spine was healed I called Lynn. "I have a lot to tell you," I said. "Most important, I have to find an apartment for myself."

"That's the best news I've heard in a long time," she said. "Come on over. You know Ernie and I will help you with anything."

I drove to Lynn's apartment that afternoon and told her all that had happened. Later she called Ernie at work and when she hung up she said, "You're staying for dinner. Ernie is bringing a friend home to meet you."

At six o'clock Ernie came in with Jules Leventhal. Jules had to be the ugliest man I'd ever seen. He was built like a prize fighter, even to the pushed-in nose. His hair and eyes were a dull brown and his skin was pock marked. After a few minutes of conversation I forgot how ugly he was because there was something so nice, so genuine about him.

I began to tell them what had happened with Frank and as the story unfolded Jules was shocked. He repeatedly interrupted my story and when I finished he said, "That guy should be knocked off for what he did to you."

"I should have left him long ago," I said, "like Ernie and Lynn told me to."

"What's done is done," Ernie said. "Never look back, Celeste."

At the end of the evening Jules drove me home. When he reached my house he said, "Celeste, I can't tell you how sorry I am for all you've been through. If you haven't turned on men forever, would you have dinner with me tomorrow night?"

The next night we went to a good seafood restaurant on the South Shore. Jules anticipated every need. He couldn't do enough for me, holding my chair, lighting my cigarettes. Just the opposite of Frank, I thought.

"Celeste, if there's anything you need, anything you want, don't hesitate to ask me," he said. Then he wrote his home phone number on the back of his business card and gave it to me.

I began going out with Jules regularly. He spent money lavishly. One night we had a lobster dinner, saw a Broadway musical, and then went to a night club.

"Celeste, I almost forgot," Jules said, taking a small box from his jacket pocket. "Here's a little gift for you."

I opened the box and there was a handsome sterling silver cigarette lighter. "Oh, Jules, that's lovely," I said. "Thank you."

On the ride home I couldn't resist saying, "You must have a money tree in your back yard."

He laughed. "I make good money as a cab dispatcher for a large company in New York. Also I'm a loan shark and a bookmaker. All the drivers are my customers."

"Wow, you must be really loaded!" I said.

"Sometimes I have it. Sometimes I don't. I like to gamble. A couple of weeks ago I bet two thousand at the track and lost it all."

"Why do you gamble?" I asked. "Everyone knows you lose more times than you win."

"There's always that chance, Celeste. If I don't win at the track, maybe I'll win betting on a football game. Some day I'm going to score."

To earn a living, I'd gone back to teaching dancing at the studio but Jules was about to change that. And I'd known him only three weeks.

"Celeste, I don't have a line," Jules said, "but I want you to know I really care for you."

"I like you, too, Jules," I said.

"What would you say if I were to set you up in an apartment and pay all the bills. Would you be my girl?"

"Why not?"

A few days later I moved into a furnished one-bedroom apartment in Queens.

"You'll have your privacy," Jules said. "I'll take you out on Wednesdays, Fridays and Saturdays."

"That's great," I said.

"There's just one thing," he said. "I want you to quit that job at the dance studio. I don't want you around all those guys."

At first I liked having my own apartment. I enjoyed the peace and quiet and it was a relief not to have to break my neck going to work every day. But in less than a week I became very lonely. And the nights I had to spend alone in the apartment made me uneasy. I'd always been afraid to be alone even for a few hours. By the end of two weeks I began to resent Jules. As a man, I found him repulsive but I had to make love to him. I quickly became accustomed to having all the bills paid. And the alternative, going back to work and spending almost all of my salary just on the necessities of life, was something I couldn't face.

It was on a double date one Wednesday night that I met a girl who was to change the course of my life. Syd was a loan shark from New York and he and Jules talked about the money they'd won and lost at the track. Lana was a very pretty platinum blond who looked about sixteen.

"I only go out with Syd when I need a good meal," she said in a lowered voice to me. "And I can see you're not exactly in love with Jules."

We both laughed. It didn't matter that the men talked horses all night. I enjoyed Lana.

"Where do you work?" I asked.

"Work?" Lana laughed. "I don't believe in it."

"Then if you're not doing anything tomorrow afternoon, come over and visit me," I said. "I don't do anything either."

Thursday afternoon Lana came over. "Nice place you've got," she said. "Is it yours?"

"Jules pays the bills," I said.

"That's a good setup if you can stand him," she said and laughed.

I told her about the years I'd lived with Frank and how it had ended. As I spoke, her eyes reflected the pain I felt.

"I'm still carrying a torch for Frank," I said.

"I know what you mean," she said. "I've been in love with Wally for two years and I always will be. He's the only man who ever really loved me. Wally was like a father to me. He's fifty years old, but it didn't make any difference. He gave me everything I wanted." Tears were in her eyes now. "I was sure he would marry me, especially after the baby, but he dropped me. He got tired of me."

"The baby?"

"I have a baby boy, two months old," she said. The tears were running down her cheeks now. "He was born with a habit," she said. "The hospital wouldn't let me keep him. They were going to place him in a foster home, but my mother took him."

"That's good," I said. "It's better if you can be with him."

She wiped her eyes. "I don't live at home," she said.

"Where do you live then?"

"Nowhere," she said.

"Well, where do you sleep?"

"Around," she laughed.

"Why don't you live with your family?" I asked.

"I could never live at home. I left as soon as I could when I was sixteen. My father made my life hell as far back as I can remember," she said.

"My father made my life rough too," I said. "He's an alcoholic."

"My father doesn't have the excuse of drinking," she said. "He's just naturally mean. He's the meanest bastard that ever lived. When I was a little kid, if I did something that bothered him, like accidently knock over a glass of milk, he'd beat me. Then while I was crying, he'd say, 'I'm going to beat you until you stop that screaming,' And he would, too."

Lana came over every afternoon after that and we became good friends. I liked Lana. She was so direct and whacky. Seeing her made it easier to put up with Jules the three nights in the week I had to be with him.

One afternoon Lana said, "Celeste, would you mind if I used your apartment this afternoon to make money with some guy?"

I laughed. "Go ahead," I said.

It was her private business and I didn't care.

She made a telephone call and an hour later a middle aged man came into the apartment. He and Lana went into the bedroom and after the man left, Lana handed me $25.

"What's this for?" I asked.

"Well, anyone I take into this apartment," she said, "seeing how it's your place, I'm going to give you half."

"Well, okay. Fine!" I said.

After that Lana called a man almost every afternoon and she always gave me half the money. One time when a guy came in, I could see right away that Lana really liked him. After he left, she said, "Celeste, I don't have any money for you this time because I can't take money from a guy if I love him."

"Love him?"

"Well, I really like Jerry, but when I'm in bed with him, I love him."

I laughed.

"I'm not a hooker at heart," she said. "I only do it when I need the money. I'm looking for love and to settle down."

Meanwhile, it was getting to be too much of an effort to put on the act with Jules three nights a week. When I mentioned it to Lana, she said, "Why do you live with him? You could have any guy you want."

"I don't know any other guy who's willing to pay the bills," I said.

Sometimes I thought of Frank and in spite of all the beatings, I still loved him. I would always love him.

Every week Jules had a gift for me. One time he gave me a silver fox jacket. He was so good to me and so generous. I didn't want to complain, but when we were out for dinner one night I told him I was bored and lonely."

"I can't stay home all day and night," I said. "If you don't want me working at the dance studio, then I'd like to enroll in an acting school. All my life I've wanted to be on the stage."

"Okay, go ahead," Jules said. "I can't expect you to stay cooped up all day."

The following week I began taking acting lessons from a married couple in New York City. Alex Brodford was a director and his wife, Emily, wrote plays. They took their work seriously. Twice a week I went to their apartment for lessons. I enjoyed those afternoons. The Brodfords were always drinking and smoking pot and I had my first joint in their place. I liked the feeling it gave me and I always smoked pot when I was with them. There were a few other young actresses and actors and it was obvious they had no money. When I walked in, they eyed my fur jacket and jewelry. Finally one day, an actress said, "You must have a rich boyfriend."

"You're right," I said.

I knew if I had to become a success on the stage the hard way, the way they were doing it, I'd quit.

One afternoon when I was in my apartment with Lana, a new man came over. Lana introduced him to me and they walked toward the bedroom. Then suddenly Lana came back into the living room.

"Celeste, Jake would rather have you. Will you go with him?"

"Why not?" I asked.

Afterwards I got to keep all the money. It was a good feeling to make $50 in fifteen minutes, but I felt low and ashamed.

A week later when Lana had a guy over, the same thing happened. He preferred me. It still made me feel guilty, but not as much as the first time.

I liked having the extra money coming in and that's when I thought of Joe Vario, a guy I'd met when I was seventeen. I'd gone out with Joe a couple of times, but I didn't care for him. He was much older than I and on our second date he had told me that he frequented prostitutes. "Celeste, if you ever want to make some money, I'll pay you to go to bed with me," he'd said. At the time I'd said, "No thanks."

Now I looked up his telephone number and called him. He was surprised to hear from me.

"Hey, Joe, remember when you propositioned me years ago?" I asked.

"Yeah, I remember," he said.

"Well, now I'm interested," I said.

"Terrific!" he said. "How about Monday night?"

I gave him my address and phone number.

Joe was already high when he picked me up Monday night. We went to a bar and after a few drinks, he was sloppy drunk. Later in the motel it was over within five minutes. Joe handed me a fistful of bills. When I got home I counted them. It came to one hundred dollars. "What a fast way to make a buck!" I thought.

The next afternoon Lana said, "Celeste, would you mind if I brought my girlfriends over to use your apartment to make some money? You'll get half the money from each of them," she said.

Now it looked like that extra money would be substantial.

The following afternoon three attractive girls came over with Lana. Renee was a statuesque redhead, Tracy a dark-haired Irish beauty, and Etran was a pretty Chinese girl.

Four men showed up that day and I made one hundred dollars and hadn't done a thing. In a month's time I had gone from prostitute to madam. The girls were over most afternoons after that and when a man came in, instead of going with the girl who had called him, he invariably asked if he could have a different girl. Now when I went with a guy, I was amazed that I didn't feel any shame at all. The johns started telling their friends about our little operation and in a few weeks we had a thing going. Now I saw a way out of the arrangement with Jules. With enough money, I could dump him. Prostitution was the answer.

Chapter IV

The Madam

The next time I saw Joe, he gave me another hundred dollars, but when he didn't call me the following week I was furious. I sensed that he would drop me suddenly and I knew I had better line up more johns fast if I wanted to dump Jules. I continued to go out with Jules three nights a week and he never suspected a thing.

Then one afternoon Tracy brought over a new girl, Dotty.

"Dotty has a book of johns for sale, if you're interested," she said.

I took the book from Dotty and after I saw all the names and telephone numbers, I gave her fifty dollars. Immediately I started calling the new johns.

The first one I reached was Artie, the jeweler. After I introduced myself and told him where I got his number, he said, "Boy, am I glad you called! Who've you got for me? I like brunettes."

"Then you'll love Tracy," I said. "She is beautiful, 38-24-34."

"I'll be there in an hour," he said.

The second john I reached was Bill the Chevy man.

"You better get over here right away, Bill," I said.

"Lana is a beautiful platinum blond and she is leaving town this evening."

"I'll be there at three-thirty," he said. "And thanks, Celeste."

That's how it went, one call after the other. And when I wasn't making calls, I was receiving them.

When Artie walked in he gave me fifty dollars, which I put in my bra. Later when Bill arrived, I introduced him to Lana. As they walked toward the bedroom, I was right behind them.

"Hey, Bill, didn't you forget something?" I asked.

He smiled and handed me fifty dollars.

"Would you like a receipt?" I asked.

The phone rang and it was Mel, the builder.

"Celeste, do you have a new girl for me?" he asked.

"Yeah, Mel. I have a beautiful Chinese girl, Etran."

"But is she any good?"

"She's dynamite action, Mel. The best in town."

"Okay, I'll be there at four-thirty."

When Bill was leaving he said, "Next time I'm bringing a friend of mine. Don't take any money from him. I'm picking up the tab. He's a customer of mine."

Early the following afternoon when the girls arrived I gave them their money. Then before the calls started coming in, I went to the bank and put the rest of the cash in a safe deposit box.

When I got back from the bank, Renee was gone.

"Where's Renee?" I asked Lana.

"Oh, she went to Manhattan to cop a bag of dope."

"Now I have to cancel her appointments!" I was furious.

My girls didn't care how much money they made, just so they had enough to stay high. If they had extra money, they took even more stuff. When Renee came back the following afternoon, I was still furious.

"Because of you, Renee, I lost money yesterday. I may even have lost a john. If you ever run off like that again, don't bother to come back!"

After that I didn't pay the girls until business was over, when all of us met late at night at a club in Greenwich Village.

One night I met my friend Natalie for dinner. I'd been seeing her about once a month for the past year and she was a friend I could confide in. She knew about Jules and that I was into prostitution now. We went to a Spanish restaurant and after we'd ordered dinner, I said, "I'm making enough dough from pros so that I can dump Jules!"

"Good riddance!" she said. Then smiling, she said, "You haven't noticed my good news!" And she held up her left hand.

"You and Nick are finally engaged!" I said. "Congratulations!"

I knew Nick only slightly. Frank and I had gone out on a double date with them long ago. As soon as I'd met Nick I felt uneasy. Although he had a terrific sense of humor, there was something about him I didn't like. Later Natalie told me he was a hit man for the Mafia. "It's just a job," she'd said. "He's really a good person."

"When's the wedding?" I asked.

"I haven't set the date yet," she said.

Friday night when Jules and I were out for dinner I said, "Jules, I don't want to go on with our arrangement any longer. I'm making it in show business and I'll be happy to pay my own way now."

"How can you walk out on me just like that?" His eyes were blazing. "After all I've done for you!"

"My mind is made up," I said.

"You were damned happy to have me around after Frank broke your back! You were damned happy when I set you up in the apartment! When you were down and out, I gave you everything your heart desired and now you want out!" His voice was getting louder and people were staring at us.

"I can't go on pretending I love you," I said.

He called the waiter and asked for the bill. He paid for the food we'd hardly touched and we left. On the way back to the apartment, Jules never stopped shouting about how ungrateful I was. When I got out of the car, he took off with the tires screeching. I didn't care how angry he was. He was out of my life and I was relieved.

That Sunday I went home for a visit. It was the first time since I'd started prostituting over a month ago, that I saw my mother. I was very uncomfortable. There was one good thing—for the first time I was able to give Mother some money. She was amazed and I said, "I told you I was going to make it big in show business." "I quit my job as a dance instructor. Now I'm making big money."

A few minutes later Grandma came over. She put her arms around me. "Celeste, I have missed you, child!" she cried.

I loved Grandma so much, but she made me feel so guilty.

"Celeste, you must obey God," she said. "Life is very short. We have only a few years on earth, but eternity is forever."

I was sorry I had gone out to Long Island now.

"Excuse me," I said. "I have to go over and see Marilyn."

I left and stayed at my sister's until I knew Grandma would be back in her own house. Then I returned to see Mother and stayed overnight.

Late Monday morning I drove back to my apartment. I went into the bedroom to change my clothes and when I opened the closet I was shocked. It was empty. All my clothes were gone. Quickly I looked through the drawers of the dresser and the fine jewelry from Jules was gone. Then, looking under the cigarette box on top of the dresser where I'd hidden three hundred dollars Saturday afternoon, I saw the cash was gone too. I walked through the apartment. The windows were locked and the door had not been forced. Jules had a key. Recalling his anger Friday night, I knew it had to be Jules.

I telephoned Natalie. Her fiance, Nick, could get everything back for me. When I told her what had happened, she said, "Tomorrow, Celeste, you and I first have to go to St. Patrick's Cathedral and pray to St. Anthony that your things will be found. Then I'll talk to Nick."

Tuesday at noon I met Natalie on the corner of Fifth Avenue and 50th Street in New York City. When we walked into the cathedral I was overwhelmed by its beauty and majesty. We went up to the main altar and knelt. I could feel the peace of God and tears rushed to my eyes. "I promise you, Lord, that I'll get out of this business soon," I said. "It's only temporary until I can get enough money."

A few minutes later we left and Natalie said, "I'll tell Nick about your problem and have him call you tonight."

At seven o'clock the phone rang.

"If you want help," Nick said, "you're going to have to see me."

"But you're Natalie's fiance," I said.

"It doesn't matter," he said. "No action, no help."

"Okay, but I don't want Natalie to ever find out about this," I said.

"Do you think I'm crazy? I love the girl!"

I went out with Nick the following night. We had a few drinks and went to a motel. When it was over he said, "I like you, Celeste, but you realize I'm in love with Natalie."

"It's all right with me," I said. "I don't want to marry you. I don't have the stomach to spend the rest of my life with a hit man."

We both laughed. Then he was serious. "Tomorrow I'll call Jules and tell him to meet us at my brother's restaurant in Little Italy at eight o'clock."

He gave me the name and address of the restaurant and drove me home. "You meet me there at seven-thirty," he said.

The next night Nick and I were sitting in the restaurant, waiting. When Jules came in I could see he was aware of the danger but still he didn't try to conceal his anger with me. He sat down and ordered a drink. Nick didn't waste a minute with small talk.

"Okay, Jules, here's what you have to do," he said. "Tomorrow night I want everything of Celeste's taken back to her apartment. The fur jacket, the clothes, the jewelry, and the three hundred dollars cash. Everything. Understand?"

"You don't know what's been going on, Nick," Jules said. "I have been paying this broad's rent for two months. I've been paying for her food, all her bills. The fur jacket and jewelry were gifts from me. I'm into shylocks for two grand because of her!"

Nick glanced at me and his eyes glinted. "In that case, Jules, just return the clothing. I'll forget the rest," he said.

When we were outside Nick said to me, "If you ripped me off like that, I'd stick a knife in your ribs and walk in your blood!"

The next day I decided to look for a larger apartment. Since I'd started calling the johns in Dotty's book, the phone had been ringing constantly. We were getting too many johns for our small place. I found a three-bedroom apartment in an attractive neighborhood. It was on the fourteenth floor and off the living room was a terrace which overlooked a park. I bought furniture and had an intercom system and two phones installed. I bought a strong box and kept it hidden behind a garment bag in the front closet. I kept the ledgers and cash in the strong box.

When I moved in I asked Lana if she'd like to live

with me.

"A place of my own!" she cried. "Oh, Celeste, you are a real friend!"

Within three weeks business had doubled and the dough had more than doubled. It was incredible what these guys would pay. I quit going to acting school in the afternoons and now went twice a week at night instead. I did little business at night because I didn't want the tenants in the building getting suspicious. I had five more girls now and I had learned that my girls were irresponsible and childish, with the exception of Tracy. She and I were the only ones not into hard drugs. I could not trust my girls and had to be in the apartment every afternoon to handle telephone calls, appointments and recommendations, the cash and the books. The girls leaned on me and looked to me for every decision. I listened to all their heartaches but I was careful not to mention my own. Although I was only twenty-four years old, they began to think of me as a pillar of strength. I laid down the law with my girls and was very strict.

Early one afternoon before any of the johns came over, I sat in the living room with eight of my girls. "I don't want any problems," I said. "I have certain rules and any girl who breaks one of them is finished!"

The girls listened without interruption. They respected me and because of my temper, some of them were afraid of me.

"No girl is allowed to rip off a john in this apartment or in a hotel date set up by me. I intend to keep this place on a first class basis and keep a good reputation. No girl is allowed to give her personal telephone number to a john. Nor can she take a john's telephone number. Any girl caught soliciting my johns for herself or anyone else, will be fired and put on my black list. Is that clear?"

The girls nodded.

"You know I can check up on you," I said. "There is an

intercom in each bedroom and I can listen in. I can also walk out on the terrace and look through the windows of two of the bedrooms."

It was only a week later that I overheard Dotty on the intercom giving her home telephone number to a john. When the john left the apartment, I exploded.

"Dotty, get out of here! You are fired and I don't ever want to see you again!"

"Oh, please, Celeste," she cried. "Give me another chance. I'm sorry. I'll never do it again. I swear!"

"In this business," I said evenly, "there can be no second chance!"

One afternoon just Renee and I were in the living room. She had been drinking for a couple of hours and now she started crying.

"I never had to get into pros," she said. "When I couldn't make it as a model, I should have gone back to Little Rock."

I had heard part of her story before and now because of the whiskey, I was going to hear all of it.

"My parents begged me to come home," she said. "If I hadn't started on heroin, I would have gone home. It got so bad there was no way to support my habit so I had to get into pros."

"Forget about what might have been, Renee," I said. "The only solution for you is to kick your habit. Then you can start all over again, go back home and lead a normal life."

"Kick my habit?" she sobbed. "That's impossible!"

She was on a real crying jag. When business was over for the day I spoke to the girls again. "There's a new rule in this house," I said. "No more liquor is to be served to the johns. And no girl is allowed to have a drink in this apartment. It's bad for business."

A few days later when I came back from the bank I found Lana and Renee in the bathroom, hitting each other with the needle. "I don't want to see drugs in this apartment!" I screamed. "You girls stash your stuff somewhere else. Have your drug parties anywhere but here. If the cops came in here and found drugs, I'd be finished!"

After that they went into the basement garage to shoot up the first fix in the afternoon.

I worried constantly about my girls getting me into trouble or trying to rip me off.

Once a week I drove to Tony's Car Wash and every time I sat in the waiting room, the owner came over to me. His name was Tony Sciortino and he was an attractive man in his late fifties with dark eyes and thick silver hair. This time as I was waiting for my car, Tony asked, "When are you going out with me?"

Instead of turning him down as I had in the past, I said, "If the price is right, I'll go out with you Tuesday night."

"Name your price," he said and smiled.

"One hundred dollars," I said.

"Tuesday at nine," he said.

I gave him my address and phone number. "Call before you come over," I said.

Tuesday night when Tony came into the apartment he looked like a different man. He had on an expensive navy suit with a white shirt and dark tie. He was wearing a gold ring with a large diamond. We went to a restaurant in Little Italy. When we walked in I was surprised when the maitre d' bowed slightly and said, "Good evening, Mr. Sciortino. How are you this evening?"

As we were led to a table in the back of the dining room, men rose to their feet and women smiled. Tony smiled briefly at each of them, but there was no warmth in his manner. I wondered why he was getting the royal treatment. We sat down and Tony said, "Celeste, you are one gorgeous broad! I've been looking for a girl like you for a long time."

Later we went to a motel and when it was over, Tony said, "Celeste, I'm going to fall for you. I know it."

He gave me a hundred dollars and asked me to go out with him Thursday night.

"How about next Tuesday?" I asked.

"A whole week?"

"I'm a madam, Tony," I said. "I can't be away from my girls too often."

He smiled. "That's a good racket," he said. "If I had your talents, that's exactly what I'd be doing."

I started going out with Tony once a week. We always went to the same restaurant and Tony was always accorded the same royal treatment. Now the patrons and waiters were treating me as if I were a celebrity. One night as we walked into the dining room, it was crowded. Every table was taken. Immediately two men got to their feet and the maitre d' signaled to a waiter who removed everything from the table, put on a new cloth and flatware—all within the space of two minutes. Tony and I sat down.

"Boy, they really jump for you!" I laughed.

Tony was clearly annoyed with my remark. "Order whatever you want," he said coldly.

Later in the motel I began to resent the time I was spending with Tony. Besides that, he was becoming emotionally involved with me and I didn't want to be bothered with that. Although I liked getting the money from him, I preferred to get my money quickly from fast tricks.

"From now on, Tony," I said, "I can see you only once every other week."

"What?" He was amazed. "Don't I pay you enough?"

"It's not that," I said. I had to be careful because I didn't want to lose him. "I just can't spend so much time away from the apartment."

One afternoon Tony called. "Celeste, if I bring two steaks over, could we have dinner in your apartment?"

"Sure," I said. "But I have Lana here with me tonight."

"Fine. Then I'll bring my friend, Victor," he said, "and four steaks."

When the men came in Victor took one look at Lana and his eyes lit up. "What a beauty!" he said.

Lana took his hand and they sat down on the couch. Tony gave me a small white box. "I've been wanting to give you something for quite a while," he said.

I opened the box and there was a gold watch from Tiffany's. "Tony, it's beautiful!" I said. "Thank you."

"It's hot," he said. "It's the best."

"The car wash business must be pretty good," I said.

His eyes flashed. "I don't discuss my business with anyone," he said.

I was startled by the harshness of his tone.

We went into the kitchen and I gave Tony a drink and started preparing the dinner. It turned out to be a terrific evening. We all enjoyed each other's company. The men especially enjoyed the steaks, french fries and salad. "This is better than eating in the restaurant," Tony said.

"It is," I said, "and I like to cook."

"Celeste, I don't know why you ever got into this business. You're too good to be doing this."

I laughed. "It's only temporary until I make it in show business," I said.

We spent the rest of the night playing cards, gambling and drinking.

"I never had so many laughs," Lana said as the men got up to leave.

"Celeste, you have a terrific setup here," Victor said. "Every other house is just hit and run. I enjoyed the whole evening."

"I want you to know I have never done this for any other johns. You and Tony are special," I said.

Tony squeezed my hand. That night I got an extra hundred dollars for broiling the steaks. After that Tony and Victor came over every other week and we had broiled steaks and an evening of gambling and laughs.

The next afternoon two of my girls and I were sitting in the living room when the doorbell rang. It was one-thirty and I wasn't expecting a john until 2 p.m. I couldn't imagine who it was and opened the door. A nice looking man in a tweed suit was standing there. He quickly walked in and smiled at the girls.

"Hi, I'm Ralph," he said.

Then his smile vanished and he pulled out a badge and said, "I'm from the vice squad."

"Oh, please don't pull us in!" I cried.

"I know all about you," he said. "This is a raid. Come on."

"Please don't do this to me!" I cried.

He looked at me for a moment. "Well, we might be able to arrange something," he said. "But it will cost you a grand."

"Oh, my God!" I cried. "Yesterday someone came in here and shook me down for everything I had. I am broke. I swear it!"

"Okay, I want some action," he said. "Then I can forget about pulling you in."

Ralph liked me the best and we went into my bedroom. When he was leaving he said, "Celeste, I'd like to see you again."

I was too scared to turn him down. "Okay," I said.

He gave me an address. "This is my friend's apartment," he said. "Meet me there Friday night at ten."

I saw Ralph a few times and he began to confide in me.

"I'm making a bundle shaking down doctors who do abortions," he said. "And I'm making even more dough with two buddies."

"Really? How?"

"Two other cops and I are making a hundred grand a year in shakedowns and resale of drugs," he said. "When we take in a kilo of heroin, we turn in a quarter of it and sell the rest and split the dough."

"Why are you telling me?" I was getting nervous.

He smiled slowly. "I figured maybe you'd like some of the action."

"Just how do I come in?" I asked. I didn't want any part of this cop and his shakedowns.

"Celeste, you could make out if you worked with us. I figure with your connections we could make a lot of dough."

I was afraid he might lock me up if I turned him down so I pretended to be interested.

"Sure," I said. "I'll start asking the girls about the dealers and I'll call you as soon as I get all the info."

Chapter V

Melanie

After the experience with the vice cop, I became security conscious. I had a police lock put on the door. No one was allowed to answer the phones or the door except me. And before opening the door now, I made sure to look through the peephole first. I couldn't trust my girls to be careful because their only interest in life was getting high.

Business was snowballing and I was making big money. And as fast as I was making it, I was blowing it. I bought more books of johns who came from Los Angeles, Chicago, Miami and cities all over the country. My house had become known to many steerers. Limousine drivers from the airports called to recommend girls. Bell hops from plush hotels sent girls to me. The best steerer of them all was Larry, a newspaper reporter for UPI. Larry knew every call girl in New York. If a girl was thrown out of a house, Larry knew about it. One afternoon he called. "Celeste, I know a terrific girl for you. Lila is the most beautiful mulatto in New York. You'll make big money through her. The guys will go crazy."

"What's her problem?" I asked.

"Ida threw her out."

Ida was a well-known madam. She was also a butch.

"Why did Ida throw her out?"

"Lila was Ida's girl and they broke up."

"Okay, Larry," I said. "Send her over."

Larry was right. Lila was a knockout.

"Lila, you have to understand one thing if you work for me," I said. "I am very careful about this house. And I am fair. I've never ripped off a john or a girl. If a girl tries to rip me off, she is through here and will find it impossible to get work in another house."

"I get the point," she said.

A few days later while two of my girls were in the bedrooms with johns, Lila and I were sitting in the living room. "Lila, watch the place for five minutes," I said. "I have to go downstairs and pay the rent."

"Sure," she said.

As I left I noticed one of my books was on the telephone table but I wasn't worried. I'd be right back. When I returned a few minutes later the book was not on the telephone table. Lila was sitting on the couch, looking through a magazine. "Where's my book?" I asked.

"What book?" she asked.

"You know damned well what book!" I screamed. "The book that was on the telephone table when I left!"

"There was no book on the telephone table," she said.

On an impulse I left the apartment, took the elevator down, and ran outside. I had a feeling that Lila had thrown the book from the terrace and was planning to pick it up later. I looked in the bushes beneath our terrace and sure enough there was the black book. As I picked it up and turned to go back into the apartment building, I saw Lila running down the street.

As soon as I was back in the apartment I called every madam I knew and told them about Lila. I was getting tired of worrying about my girls ripping me off. I couldn't trust any of them. They were into hard drugs and would do anything to get more money or save their own necks. I had girls rotating, working in other houses then returning to me. If there was a raid in a house where one of my girls was working, I worried that if she was arrested while there, she would turn me in so she could go free. The cops made these deals with prostitutes all the time. If a prostitute didn't turn in a madam, she'd turn in a drug dealer.

Later that day when business was over I talked to my girls and told them what Lila had done. "She'll never find work again in a house," I said. This frightened the girls because if they couldn't work in a house they would have to hit the streets.

"And remember," I added, "if I ever get a complaint from a john, if he doesn't like a girl, it's her fault. When a john walks in here, you have to make him feel like the most important guy in the world! And another thing, never complain in front of a john. It's bad for business. You can become an expert at putting on a smile, no matter how you feel."

No john was aware of the bitterness in my heart. I didn't want to scare them away.

One afternoon Fern called. She was a madam from uptown New York. "Celeste, I have a beautiful girl, Melanie, but I can't keep her any longer and I will not put her out on the street."

"What's her problem?"

"She's got a $200-a-day habit, but she is the most lovable kid I've ever known. Please see her just once."

"Okay," I said. "Send her over, but I don't like junkies. They're trouble."

One hour later Melanie was at the door. I couldn't believe she was a prostitute. She was the most beautiful girl I had ever seen. More startling than her beauty, though, was her refinement. And there was an incredible innocence about her. Large soulful grey eyes glowed in her finely chiseled face. Thick, glossy dark hair and long lashes were set off by her smooth ivory complexion. She stood there hesitantly.

"Come on in, Melanie," I said, smiling, trying to reassure her. "Sit down and we'll talk."

She walked into the dining room with me. She was petite, delicately formed, almost fragile. We sat down at the table and I knew before she said a word that I would take her in.

"I need a place to stay," she said in a soft voice, "not just work."

"I know," I said. "And you can move in and live with me."

"I can?" Her eyes sparkled. "Oh, Celeste, thank you!"

When she smiled she was even more beautiful. Her teeth glistened and little dimples played at the corners of her mouth. There was a child-like quality about her.

I explained the house rules to her and she nodded now and then in understanding. She wasn't one to waste words. When I finished talking I said, "Melanie, how did you get into pros?"

She was the most unlikely candidate I had ever met. I couldn't imagine how a girl so refined, so sensitive, had gotten into this racket.

She studied me and decided I really wanted to know.

"When I was a kid my family lived in a tenement in New Jersey. My father drank and couldn't hold a job. We never had any heat and sometimes we didn't have electricity. My mother tried to make things easier for my brother and me. She was a very good person but she had her own problems. My father beat her and she was always crying. My brother and I tried to comfort her but the older we got the worse things got. My father paid no attention to Dick or me when we were little. Then when I was ten years old my father raped me."

She drew in her breath sharply, but in a moment she

was under control again.

"After that I ran away but the police found me wandering around and took me back home. I never told my mother or anyone else. My father raped me many times. I was afraid to fall asleep at night. I kept running away but every time the police found me and took me home." Tears were in her eyes, but she went on with the story in that soft voice. "When I was fourteen I started going out with a boy and got pregnant. I went to a home for unwed mothers. I had a beautiful baby girl and when she was a week old, a family adopted her. Then I went back home and by that time Dick was shooting heroin and selling it. He was busted and went to prison. He's been in and out of prison for years now. When I was sixteen I dropped out of school and left home. I took a job as a receptionist in a beauty salon. Within a year I was shooting heroin. To get the money for my habit, I had to start prostituting."

"What about your family, do you ever see them?" I asked.

"I haven't seen them in four years and they've never tried to locate me. I could never go home again."

I got up and put my arm around her. "I'll take care of you, Melanie," I said.

With those words the control went out of her and she began to sob and clung to me like a child. I vowed that as long as I knew her, no one else was going to hurt her. When she had calmed down, we went into the living room and I introduced her to the girls. They took to her immediately and without knowing anything about her, they all assumed the big sister role.

In the following days as we sat there talking, I noticed that Melanie never once mentioned her past. The other girls complained constantly and given the slightest encouragement, they would start crying and going through a whole lifetime of bad breaks that led to prostitution. This was why I insisted that all my girls meet every night at a club in the Village. The biggest problem I had to fight in them and in myself was depression. And the only way to fight it was to keep moving, keep drinking and laughing. Every night my girls wore the most beautiful clothes, had their hair done in the latest style, and we met at the club around midnight. As soon as we arrived they would cop a few bags of dope and go to the ladies' room and hit each other with the needle. At night they took twice as much to get high. Some of them snorted cocaine. We went from one bar to another and finally to an after hours club and stayed out until 5 a.m. We never did any business after midnight. We were out to forget. Sometimes I drank too much.

"Celeste, you're not the same person when you drink," Lana said to me one day. "You get nasty. You hurt people's feelings. You're like a general in the army—all orders!"

"I don't mean to be that way," I said.

But as time passed I drank more and more heavily. It was the only way I could cope with what I was doing. And I was aware that little by little I was losing control of my life. The thing that held me together was the belief that some day Prince Charming would walk through the door, fall madly in love with me and take me out of this sordid business.

After Melanie had been with us a couple of weeks I took her to visit my family. Whenver I went home it was as though my real life ceased to exist. Melanie and I went into the house and when I introduced Melanie, Mother hugged her. Melanie was so touched the tears came to her eyes. As we went through the living room into the kitchen, Dad was sitting in his armchair, stoned. He didn't even notice us. We sat down and I gave Mother a hundred dollar bill. She was so grateful, she couldn't speak. I wanted to take care of Mother. I wanted to make up to her for all the things she'd gone without. And now, finally,

I was going to be able to do it. Later we had cheese ravioli and baked peppers and a salad. Melanie enjoyed every minute and insisted on doing the dishes for Mother.

In the early evening Grandma came over. With Melanie there I thought Grandma might refrain from talking about the Lord but nothing could stop her. When I introduced Melanie, Grandma took both her hands and said, "Melanie, do you know that Jesus loves you?"

Melanie smiled but didn't say anything.

Then Grandmother looked at me with those beautiful brown eyes and said, "Celeste, Jesus has told me that some day you'll be working for Him as an evangelist!"

"Excuse me," I said. "I'm going to make a pot of coffee."

Melanie followed me into the kitchen and winked. "How do you like that?" she whispered. "Madam turned evangelist!"

After we'd left and were driving back to Queens, Melanie said, "You're so lucky to have such a nice family."

"Yes," I said. I didn't say anything about my father.

"But tell me, does your grandmother really believe Jesus talks to her?"

"Oh, yes," I said.

"What religion is she?" Melanie asked.

"It's not a religion," I said. "Grandma is a born again Christian and Jesus literally lives in her heart."

"And what do you think about that, Celeste?"

"I think it's beautiful," I said. "When I was a little girl I promised the Lord I would serve Him. Some day when I go straight and get married and have kids, I'll work for the Lord."

"Well, I'm a Catholic," she said, "and I'll die a Catholic."

That night before I fell asleep I prayed. "Oh, God, forgive me for the life I'm leading," I said. "I don't want to do this, but there's no other way for me. Some day when I'm eighty years old I'll serve You, I promise."

Melanie was so grateful that I'd taken her in, she

couldn't do enough for me. She did the grocery shopping and wouldn't let me work in the kitchen. Whenever I went out and asked her to come with me, she was more than willing. Soon she had become my shadow. What she and none of the other girls suspected was that I had an unreasonable fear of being alone.

One Saturday afternoon in October I asked Melanie to go to Manhattan with me.

"I'd like to," she said. "I need to buy a couple of dresses and it's hard to find what I like because I'm so small."

As we were walking down 34th Street, every head turned to look at us, but their eyes lingered on Melanie. As she walked, her thick, dark hair bounced and glistened in the autumn sunlight. She stopped suddenly and said, "Wait a minute." Then reaching in her pocketbook she took out a fifty dollar bill and handed it to a beggar.

When we were a few yards away from the man, I said, "Melanie, you shouldn't give that much money away. When you need it, no one is going to help you."

"I'd just spend it on something frivolous," she said. "It's better I give it to someone who really needs it."

After we'd been shopping for a few hours we started back toward the car. In the window of a music store I saw a man playing an organ. We stopped to look.

"That man is not reading sheet music," I said. "He's reading numbers."

We went into the store and I asked him how he could play the organ without notes. When he explained the number system of playing, I said, "You mean anyone can play like that?"

"That's right, Miss," he said.

Immediately I ordered an organ.

Four days later when the organ arrived I was the only one in the living room. Lana was in a bedroom with a john. Two men moved the organ against the back wall of the living room. As soon as they left, I sat down at the organ and opened the booklet to "Ave Maria." I began to play slowly and within a few minutes to my astonishment I was able to play smoothly. I experimented with the pedals and learned to coordinate them with the notes. When I had the hang of it, I started playing "Ave Maria" over again, this time with feeling and power. The chords swelled, filling the apartment. It was beautiful. I was half way through the hymn when the john, a young Italian, came out of the bedroom almost in tears.

"Gee, Celeste, do you think you should play church music in a place like this?"

"Vinnie, I was only trying to learn to play by this new number system," I said. "I think it sounds beautiful!"

Within two minutes he had left the apartment. Lana came into the living room, holding her stomach and laughing hysterically. "Playing church music in a house of prostitution!" she screamed. She laughed so hard she fell on the floor.

Chapter VI

Evelyn

When I went to Brodford's for my acting lesson the following Thursday night, Alex greeted me with a big smile.

"Celeste, the play we've been rehearsing in the past few months is going to be showcased off Broadway in two weeks!"

"Alex, that's terrific!"

Finally, I was going to have my big chance. If this play were successful, maybe I'd get into acting full time. The play was about a psychiatrist who invited his patients to a cocktail party to act out their inhibitions and frustrations.

On opening night, Tony, Victor and Lana were in the audience. Later when we went out to celebrate, Tony said, "Celeste, I wouldn't be surprised if you became a big star!"

But the critics didn't like the play. It ran three nights and closed. One critic wrote, "Although the writing left much to be desired and the play had little significance, Celeste Clemente is a young actress to be watched!"

Despite those glowing words, I lost my enthusiasm for the stage. Making money as an actress was too uncertain. After that I dropped out of acting school.

The next time Tony and Victor came over, Tony was

carrying a large white box. "What's in there?" I asked.

"I thought you needed a little cheering up after the play folded," he said.

I opened the box and gasped. There was a white mink coat. "Tony, it's gorgeous!" I cried.

"It's hot," he said and laughed.

I put the coat on and walked around the living room as they watched.

"It was made for you, Celeste," Tony said. "It's perfect with your black hair and dark, flashing eyes."

I looked in the hall mirror. It was the most beautiful mink coat I'd ever seen.

At the end of the evening as the men were leaving, Tony said, "Celeste, I really love you. I wish you'd spend more time with me alone."

"Tony, you can understand," I said. "I can't spend time away from the business."

"You're right," he said.

After they'd left Lana said, "I wish I had a boyfriend who would give me a mink." Her expression changed and she added, "Seriously, Celeste, I'm happy for you. You deserve the best."

When I got into bed that night I thought not only do I deserve the best, but I have the best. I had beautiful clothes, a Cadillac, fine jewelry, and now a mink. I had big money coming in steadily, but for the first time it hit me that none of this made any difference. The best wasn't enough. It didn't matter how much I had of worldly goods, there was a large vacuum in my life that nothing and no one could fill.

The next afternoon as the girls and I sat around talking, Tracy said, "Celeste, as a favor to me, would you give a friend of mine a chance to work for you?"

"What's her problem?" I asked.

"Evelyn is into drugs. She used to be a high class call girl. A few years ago she came into an inheritance and moved from Delaware to New York. She wanted to see what life in the big city was like. She found out soon. She spent her money like crazy and one day a friend offered her some coke. Evelyn liked it so much she became hooked. In a year's time she'd blown all her money and when her money ran out, her friends ran out. She had to have the coke so she started hustling in a house. Months later she met a black pimp and got turned on to him. Later he turned her on to heroin. Within a year her veins had collapsed from the injections and she had tracks all over her arms, legs and breasts. By this time no madam would have her. Ida was the last one to throw her out. Now Evelyn is hustling in the streets."

I knew the girl would be nothing but trouble, but I couldn't say no.

"Maybe she'll work out," I said. "I'll give her a try."

"Oh, thanks, Celeste!" Tracy said. "You won't be sorry. I promise."

The next afternoon Tracy brought Evelyn to the apartment. The girl had a pretty face but she was emaciated.

"Show me your tracks," I said.

She changed into a robe and I took one quick look. The sight was horrible.

"As long as you keep yourself covered with high-necked dresses and long sleeves, and when you're in the bedroom keep the lights out, you can work for me," I said.

"Celeste, I really appreciate your giving me this chance," she said. "You're really good hearted."

Two weeks later I had set up dates for Lana, Melanie, Evelyn and myself. We were going to meet four johns in a hotel in midtown. Lana and Melanie were getting dressed when Evelyn came in at 9 p.m.

"We'll be ready in a minute, Evelyn," I said.

"Okay," she said and sat down on the couch.

I went to the bathroom and a minute later when I came out, she was nowhere to be seen. I looked in the bedrooms but she wasn't there. I ran to the telephone table where I'd left my bag. All the cash I had, $800, was gone. I took the elevator downstairs and ran into the street. It was too late. Evelyn was gone.

If I had to watch my girls so I wouldn't be ripped off, I had to watch Melanie so she wouldn't give all her money away. She still continued to give large bills to every beggar she saw. And whenever one of the girls was low on cash, Melanie would immediately take out her wallet and give half her money to the girl.

I took her aside one day. "Melanie, you have to start thinking of yourself. There's no point in making all this money if you're going to give it away. And these girls are not going to reimburse you when they have it."

"I already found they forget," she said.

"Melanie, from now on I'm going to hold half your money. When you need it, I'll give you whatever you want."

"That's a good idea," she said. "Then I'll always have enough for a fix."

That was her only interest in life. She shot up more than the other girls at night and always came out of the ladies' room at the club giggling. I talked to her about kicking her habit, but she just smiled and said, "I'll never go straight. I dig getting high. It makes me forget my crazy life."

One night instead of going to the after hours club in the Village, the girls and I went to a nightclub not far from my apartment. It was a different crowd. There were no Broadway stars, no Playboy bunnies and no johns. Just ordinary people. A young man came up to me and asked me to dance. He was lean and muscular and had a strong face and steady grey eyes. His name was Steve Mabrey.

"What do you do?" I asked him.

"I'm in construction," he said. "The pay is good."

I wondered what he'd think if he knew how much money I was making. We sat together at a table away from the girls and Steve ordered a gin and tonic for himself and a Scotch and water for me. He never took his eyes from my face. He'd hardly touched his drink when I'd finished mine. He ordered another Scotch for me.

"You're not a drinker," I said.

"I drink a little, not much." He smiled. "Do you mind?"

"Mind? I think it's great!" I took out a cigarette and he held out his lighter.

"I bet you don't smoke pot," I said.

"I've never wanted to," he said. "I'm straight."

I had forgotten there were any straight guys. Later when I told him I had to leave, he said, "Will you go out with me Friday night?"

Because he was such a decent guy I had to tell him the truth. "Steve, you wouldn't want to take me out. I'm a hooker."

He looked at me steadily. "Celeste, I don't care. I like you and I want to take you out."

I gave him my telephone number and said, "Well, maybe some day."

The next night he called and he kept calling, but I wouldn't go out with him. I didn't see the sense of getting involved with a nice guy when I could be making big money. But the freak scenes and the pressures were getting to me and one night a couple of weeks later when Steve called, I was so depressed, so fed up with everything, I was glad to go out with him.

"You're not the type to be a hooker," he said over dinner.

I laughed. "That's what everyone says."

When we left the restaurant he said, "Celeste, I want you to come back to my apartment with me."

I shook my head.

"I'll pay you anything you ask if that's the only way I can have you."

"I couldn't take money from you, Steve," I said.

We went to his apartment but after I was back in my place I felt guilty. It wasn't right for a nice guy to get involved with a hooker. After that he called me every night. I went out with Steve several times and enjoyed his company. While I was with him I forgot the sordid life I was leading. After all the degenerates I'd known, his goodness and honesty opened up a new world for me.

One time when we were in his apartment, he said, "Celeste, when I met you it didn't bother me that you were a hooker."

"And now you're jealous?"

"Now I love you," he said. "I want to marry you."

"Marry me! You would be willing to marry me, knowing what I am?"

"I don't care what you've done," he said. "Just so you're faithful to me from now on."

Tears stung my eyes. "I don't think we ought to see each other again, Steve," I said and left.

Before falling asleep that night I cried. Finally I had met a man who would take me out of this way of life, a man who would make a wonderful husband. But I couldn't settle for a normal life now. I was making too much money to give it up. Yet, if I had the chance I would give up all the money and go back to Frank. It was six months since that night he'd broken my back. I still loved him and deep down I thought that one day, somehow, I would get him back.

A week later I received a call from Ida. I had come to dread her calls. When no other madam would take a girl, Ida called me. She knew I could not turn down a girl. But I was in for a surprise. She didn't want me to take anyone.

"Celeste, you won't believe the girl I've got working for me!" she said in that deep, throaty voice.

"Who?" I asked.

"Hally Woods!" she said.

"The same Hally Woods who did the centerfold in Playboy Magazine?"

"The very same!" Ida laughed. "This girl is so great that my phones have been ringing night and day. Everybody is asking for her."

"How did you ever get her?"

"I stole her from her pimp!" Ida said. "She smartened up and left him. He beat her once too often. I met her at a gay bar. She had gone there with a friend out of curiosity. She didn't know anything about gay life. I brought her home with me and I was good to her. After the treatment she'd been getting from her pimp, she appreciated me. Now she's mine and we've got a good thing going between us!"

"More power to you," I said, but I had an uneasy feeling about Ida stealing this girl from the pimp.

A few days later I called Ida to warn her about a girl who had stolen another madam's books. Then I said, "How are you doing with Hally?"

"Her pimp was here yesterday," she said. "He insisted Hally go back to him, but she refused. Then he said to me, 'I'll give you twenty-four hours to kick her out!'" Ida laughed. "I'm not worried. He's got ten other girls working for him."

Two days later Lana handed me a newspaper, pointing to a story she'd circled. "Read that," she said.

The headline was, *Woman's Body Found in East River.* Quickly I read through the story. Police had checked the fingerprints and identified the body as being that of Ida Berrigan. Miss Berrigan, the story stated, had a history of arrests dating back to 1950 for running a brothel.

"My God!" I cried. "I could end up the same way!"

That night I couldn't fall asleep. What kind of crazy world had I gotten into? Looking back on the past months I realized that every day, every person I was involved with was a potential threat. I had to be on my toes every minute. In the apartment, in the street, in restaurants, in nightclubs. No place was safe and no one could be trusted. First it was Ralph, the shakedown cop, then Lila trying to steal a book of johns, then Evelyn stealing $800, and now Ida murdered. Everything in my world revolved around money, big money. And I was making more money than any madam in the New York area.

Running to clubs every night, drinking, smoking pot was no longer enough to combat the depression that was swamping me. I decided what I needed was a vacation.

A couple of days later I said to Melanie, "How would you like to go to Puerto Rico?"

"Would I!"

"Get ready then!" I said.

"When are we going?" she asked.

"As soon as I can get reservations," I said.

She laughed. I called the airport and they had two seats available on a flight leaving the next night.

When Melanie and I landed in San Juan we took a cab to the Caribe Hilton Hotel. As soon as we were in the room I said, "Melanie, we are on vacation. I am here to forget what I am. If anyone asks what I do, I'm saying I'm in medical school, or a struggling actress, whatever I feel like being."

She laughed. "I'm going to art school myself," she said. "I always wanted to be an artist."

We changed into cocktail dresses and went down to the lounge. We weren't there two minutes when a man came over to the table. "Hello, girls," he said. "Mind if I join you?"

"Be my guest," I said.

He was a middle-aged man, heavy set. "My name is Manny Siegel," he said. "I'm a movie producer."

"How nice!" I said.

Manny signaled the waiter and ordered drinks. Then he

motioned to another man who had just come into the lounge. "You girls will like Jake," he said. "He's a script writer for MGM."

Jake was in his late thirties and when he saw Melanie, his eyes widened for a moment. Then, regaining his composure, he smiled. "Always glad to meet beautiful girls," he said.

I knew where this was leading.

"What do you do, Celeste?" Manny asked.

"I'm in my third year of law school," I said.

He laughed outright. "Pardon me. I'm not laughing at you, but a girl as beautiful as you in law school!"

"It's true," I said. My acting lessons were paying off because instead of finding it amusing, Manny was now let down.

"I could get you into movies," he said.

"I'm not interested," I said. "I have to work with my brain or I'm bored."

Jake had been questioning Melanie and she was telling him about her home in East Hampton, Long Island. "We live on the water," she said. "My father is a neurosurgeon in New York."

Manny interrupted the conversation. "Melanie, would you like to make it in Hollywood?"

She laughed delicately. "I'm finishing art school this spring," she said. "I wouldn't be happy doing anything but painting."

"What a waste!" Manny said.

In a short time the men left. Melanie and I went into the dining room and ordered dinner. And for the rest of the night we had to play our little game with the men who approached us. Having to lie all night was a strain and a constant reminder of my real life. When we got back to our room I said to Melanie, "I came down to Puerto Rico to forget but I guess there's no place I'll ever be able to forget!"

"I really don't care," she said. "Doing it or trying to forget, it's all the same. There's no way out."

The following afternoon we put on our bathing suits and went to the beach in front of the hotel.

"If I just get a tan, I'll be happy," I said.

I closed my eyes and felt the warmth of the sun's rays. Minutes later a man's voice broke the silence. "Miss America!" he said.

I opened my eyes and looked up into a darkly tanned face with a sparkling smile. "I'm Fernando Lopez," he said and sat down next to me. He didn't waste any time letting me know how much he was worth. "I own a sugar planta-tion in Puerto Rico," he continued, "and real estate all over the Island. I'm divorced and you might say I'm the answer to the American girl's dream."

I thought he was lying. "I'm just a struggling actress," I said.

"Would you girls like to see my plantation?" he asked.

"That might be fun," I said.

We went back to the hotel room, showered and changed into street clothes. Fernando was waiting for us in the lobby. When we were inside his Lincoln, I nudged Melanie and she winked. We drove a few miles and when Fer-nando parked his car I realized he had not been lying. We looked over the plantation and then drove to his home. He called a friend of his on the phone.

"Enrico will join us for dinner," he said.

A half hour later Enrico arrived and the four of us went to a restaurant overlooking the ocean.

"We're going to show you girls the sights of San Juan," Fernando said. He was very considerate and attentive but I could see right away he was a drinker. He was sip-ping martinis like high balls. By the time dinner arrived Fernando was high. After dinner he had two quick drinks before we left to go to a nightclub. When we had a table Fernando took my hand. "Celeste, you're the kind of girl I've been looking for," he said.

I smiled. "Thank you," I said.

"I'm serious," he said.

We danced and laughed but Fernando was guzzling high balls faster than any of the drinkers in New York. By midnight he could hardly stand. I refused to dance with him again.

"I'm sorry," he said. "I'll make it up to you. I'll tell you what. I'll pick up the tab for you and Melanie as long as you're in San Juan. The hotel bill, everything."

"I'll have to think about it," I said.

When it was time to leave, Enrico drove us back to the hotel. Fernando had passed out in the back seat.

The next day Fernando called but I refused to see him.

"I'll still pick up the tab," he said. "I'm serious, Celeste, I really like you."

I felt sorry for him. I knew he liked me but I couldn't get involved with such a heavy drinker. I didn't care how much money he had. "Call me tomorrow," I said.

The following night Melanie and I went out with Fernando and Enrico. After dinner we went to Fernando's house. He mixed drinks and put on the stereo. After we'd been dancing awhile, he said, "Celeste, we haven't known each other very long but I want to marry you." He was serious.

"I'm sorry, Fernando," I said, "but I have a steady boyfriend in New York."

"If you ever change your mind, let me know," he said.

"We're going back to New York tomorrow night," I said.

I gave him my address and telephone number. "Maybe we'll come back to San Juan for another vacation," I said.

"I hope so," he said.

When we were back in the hotel room, I told Melanie about the proposal. "If the guy wasn't such an alcoholic, I'd consider it," I said.

"I wouldn't," she said. "I wouldn't marry any man.

There isn't one of them who is worth it." She spoke in that soft voice without a trace of bitterness.

The next afternoon we went to the beach. We were there a short time when I saw Manny walking along the edge of the surf in our direction. When he saw us, he came over. "I've been calling you, Celeste," he said. "Why haven't you returned my calls?"

"I've been busy," I said.

Manny sat down and once again began talking about getting me into movies.

"Can't I convince you I'm not interested?"

"Celeste, I'll believe that, but please before I go back to L.A., will you go to bed with me? I'll give you any amount you want."

"I don't have to go to bed with a man I don't love," I said. "I have plenty of money. My father is a highly successful criminal attorney."

Melanie got up and ran into the water.

The more I said no, the more Manny kept after me. Finally he stood up and said, "I'm flying back to the coast tonight." He threw his wallet in my lap. "Take whatever you want," he said.

I took out four one hundred dollar bills, stood up and went with him to his hotel room. When it was over I was disgusted with myself. I'd come to Puerto Rico to forget what I'd been doing in New York and here I was doing the same thing again. I couldn't even play a part. There was no way out, not even for a weekend. It was as though an outside force had control of my life.

Chapter VII
The Arrest

When I got back to New York I was more depressed than when I'd left. I found it almost impossible to listen patiently to my girls when they needed to talk about their problems. It was getting harder and harder to put on a smile for the johns. When Tony called and wanted to come over with Victor, I thought that might help.

While we were enjoying our steak dinner, Lana suddenly started laughing. "Would you like to hear what I did this afternoon?" she asked.

"What did you do?" I asked.

"I almost gave my father a heart attack!" she said. She hit the table with her hand and started laughing again. "I got in my convertible and drove with the top down. Then I saw a big black man hitchhiking. I picked him up and drove over to where my father works in a gas station. Sure enough Daddy was out there. I drove by nice and slow. It just killed Daddy! It just killed him!"

Victor and Tony laughed but I had to force myself to laugh. After dinner we played blackjack and I was raking in money from Lana and the men.

"This is your night!" Lana said.

"I could still lose," I said.

But after a couple of hours I had won $800. "See that? God always pays me back what I lose. Last month one of my girls went through my bag and stole $800 and then disappeared."

"Gee, Celeste, you sure are lucky," Tony said. "I'd like to take you to the track."

Nights spent with Tony and Victor had always refreshed me, but not this time. After they left I was as down as before they'd come in.

"What's the matter with you?" Lana asked.

"I don't know," I said. "I guess this business is getting to me."

Early the next afternoon I called Mother.

"When are you coming home for a visit?" she asked.

"Maybe this weekend, Mother," I said.

Then in the background I could hear Grandma's voice raised. "Celeste, Jesus loves you!" she cried.

"Mother, I have to go," I said and hung up.

Grandma would never stop. I just wouldn't call home again except late at night when I knew Grandma would be in her own house.

A week later Tony took me to a restaurant in Little Italy. Before dinner I had finished three martinis. "Don't overdo it tonight," he said. The last time we'd been out he'd gotten angry because I drank too much and became very loud.

"Tony, sometimes you can be a pain," I said.

"That's a nice way to talk when I have a beautiful gift for you," he said.

"I'm sorry," I said. "I'll try not to drink too much."

He took a small box from his jacket pocket and put in on the table. I opened the box and inside was a jewelry box. I pressed the lock and it sprang open. I was stunned. It was a diamond necklace. "Tony, that is beautiful! Thank you!"

I put it on and glanced in my compact mirror. "It's

the most beautiful thing I've ever seen!" I cried.

He smiled. "You get such a kick out of everything!" he said. "That's why I like to give you presents."

After dinner we went to a nightclub in the same neighborhood. And even though I was grateful for the diamond necklace, once I started drinking, I couldn't stop.

A couple of hours later Tony said, "Celeste, I'm taking you out of here before you fall on your face."

He had me firmly by the arm and through the haze of alcohol I realized he was angry, but I didn't care. I remembered getting into his car, but that's all.

The next afternoon Chet Rainor, one of my favorite johns, called. "Celeste, I'd like you to meet Wendy. I think she'd work out for you. "She's eighteen and she's a gorgeous redhead."

"Okay, Chet. Send her over," I said.

If Chet liked her, she must be pretty good.

Wendy arrived early that evening. She had naturally curly red hair and beautiful clear green eyes. We sat in the living room and she told me about herself. "I'm tired of giving my body away for nothing," she said. "If I can get paid for it, why not? Every man is out for one thing anyhow."

"What went wrong?" I asked.

"I just have to get away from home," she said. "My mother's all right, but I hate my father. All my life he has ignored me. He's always given me money but nothing else. Even when I had the lead in a play in tenth grade, he wouldn't come to the school. He stayed home to watch TV." She started crying as though it had happened yesterday. "My father is always busy with his bagel business. And when he's home, my mother and I aren't allowed to speak. He's glued to the TV. When I was drinking and staying out late and skipping school, he didn't care. But when I dropped out of school in eleventh grade, he blew his top. Too late!"

My heart went out to Wendy.

"Then last week when I told him I was leaving home and was going to be a prostitute, he said, 'After all the money I've given you, why would you want to do a thing like that?' "

"What about your mother? She must be very upset."

"Oh, she carried on when I left, but she'll be all right. She's been seeing some guy for the last few months and I think she's going to leave my father. I hope she does."

"Wendy, you can start working for me tonight," I said.

"Gee, thanks, Celeste! That's terrific!"

"I think you'll make out very well," I said. "You can make a lot of dough."

Later I sent out for two chicken dinners and after that Wendy was more relaxed. While I was telling her the house rules, the telephone rang. I picked up the receiver and I could hear music in the background. A strong masculine voice came through. "Hello, Celeste, this is Jack Duffy. I got your number from Ellis Willard."

Ellis was one of our highest paying johns from out of town.

"How is Ellis?"

"He's fine and sends his regards. Listen, Celeste, I just got into town and I'm at the Twenty-One Club. I was wondering if you could meet me at my hotel later tonight and bring a girl with you."

I was on the verge of saying no when he added, "How about $400 for the night?"

"Okay," I said. For that kind of dough, I'd take a chance.

"I'll be in room 8928 at the Park Sheraton. Meet me there at eleven."

"See you at eleven with Wendy," I said. "She's a dream!"

When I hung up I felt something was wrong but I dismissed the feeling. Jack Duffy sounded like a really nice guy.

"Wendy, you'll have your first trick tonight," I said.

"Great!" she said.

We went downstairs to the beauty salon and had our hair done. By ten-thirty I was dressed in a pink lame' cocktail gown. Wendy had on a green silk dress of mine that just matched her eyes. She looked beautiful. "You're all right," I said to her.

On the way uptown in a cab, I tried to push the nagging fear from my mind that this guy might be a cop. Ellis should have brought him over personally.

When we arrived at room 8928, there were two nice-looking guys in their mid-thirties. "Hi, I'm Jack," the taller one said. "And this is my buddy, Mike O'Connor."

We introduced ourselves and when Jack took our coats he and Mike eyed us appreciatively. I began to relax.

"Celeste, you certainly have the hardware!" Jack said as he poured champagne into glasses on the coffee table.

Mike was talking to Wendy and she was laughing. After we'd had a few glasses of champagne, my fears were gone.

"Celeste, I'd like to pay you now," Jack said.

"Okay," I said.

He handed me four one hundred dollar bills. I put the cash in my wallet and then he pulled out a badge. "You're under arrest, girls!"

"What?" I cried.

Wendy bolted from the room and Mike ran after her.

"How did you find out about me?" I cried.

"A tenant in your building complained about traffic going in and out of your apartment," he said.

"Oh, God!" I cried.

I was scared but at the same time, strangely, I felt a vast sense of relief. Wendy was back in the room with Mike. She was crying hysterically.

"Calm down, Wendy," Mike said. "It's not the end of the world."

She finally stopped crying and we put on our coats and

left the room with the two cops. We went down in the elevator and out to the unmarked police car. On the ride to the precinct I said to Jack, "You don't know how glad I am I was caught! I thank God this is over! I could not have gone on with this business much longer!"

When we were in the precinct the sergeant at the desk asked for our names.

"Do I have to give my real name?" I asked.

"Yes, Miss, and identification."

"Oh, my God!" I cried. "I don't want my family to find out about this!"

"You're a very lucky girl," the sergeant said. "There isn't a paper in New York that can print a word about your arrest. There's a city-wide newspaper strike."

"Thank God!" I said.

If my family ever knew what I'd been doing, it would kill them.

We were finger-printed and mug shots were taken. Then I was put in a small cell with a junkie. The girl was cursing and talking to herself and didn't even notice me come in. She seemed delirious. Wendy was put in the next cell with another junkie, who was also muttering and carrying on. The only person who seemed the least bit normal was a girl in a cell across the corridor.

"Hey, baby, what'd ya get busted for?" she asked.

"Pros and procuring," I said.

"Oh, well, you should be glad they didn't find any coke on you. Then you'd be doing heavy time. You got a cigarette?"

I threw her a cigarette. "I'm Celeste," I said.

"I'm Debra," she said.

The other girl in Debra's cell was holding onto the bars and she was moaning. I thought these girls were putting on a show. I caught Wendy's eye and we both started laughing. I wasn't laughing long. The girl in my cell started throwing up on the floor.

"They all need a fix," Debra said. "You haven't seen anything yet."

A couple of hours later junkies in other cells were throwing up and moaning. Before the night was over I thought I was in a lunatic asylum. And I couldn't understand how the guards pacing the corridor could ignore such suffering. I looked at the girl lying on the cot in my cell. She was the most horrible sight I'd ever seen. She had very little hair and I could see her scalp. Her teeth were black and quinine burns covered her legs. She looked up at me.

"One time I was on top like you," she said. "I was a high-class call girl, but now I'm walking the streets, getting $5 a trick and all the money I can steal. Just for drugs. I'd be better off dead!"

I had to turn away from her. This will never happen to me, I vowed. I am going to get out of this business! I am going to get away from these people!

In the morning the policewoman let us out of the cells. "Come on girls, you're going to court," she said.

I walked down the hall with her. "Why don't they do something for these junkies?" I asked. "They should be in a hospital, not a jail."

"The law does not permit us to give medication without a doctor's prescription," she said, "and the city budget is too tight to hire a doctor for a jail."

We were put in a police van and taken to Prostitution Court at 100 Center Street, New York City. Then in the courthouse we were put in the bull pen, where we waited to be seen by the judge. The police started bringing in more girls who'd been arrested for prostitution the night before. I saw several girls who had once worked for me. Their habits had become so bad I had to stop using them. Now they had hit the streets.

I was permitted to make one telephone call and I called a noted pros lawyer, Murray Weinstein. He said he'd be over within an hour.

When he arrived he said, "Celeste, you don't have a thing to worry about. Because this is your first offense, you won't do any time. You'll get a suspended sentence, but you will be convicted."

At eleven o'clock we went into the courtroom. It looked like a kangaroo court to me. With each girl it was the same procedure—in and out, guilty or not guilty. The judge's voice never changed. He spoke in the same monotone to each girl and seldom bothered to look at her. He just made notes on a piece of paper. Although Weinstein had said the judge was okay, I was scared. Finally my name was called and I went forward with Weinstein and stood before the judge.

"Are you Celeste Clemente?" the judge asked without looking at me.

"Yes, your honor," I said.

"You are charged with prostitution and procuring. How do you plead?"

"Not guilty, your honor."

"Case adjourned until March 14 at 9:30 a.m. for trial. Bail is set at $500. Next case."

My lawyer put up the money for bail and when I walked out of that courtroom a free woman I swore I was through with prostitution forever! The junkies, the degenerates, and the danger I'd been living with was finally over! I'd been a prostitute for six months, but it seemed like fifty years. Now I could lead a normal life. I would find a job, meet a rich man, get married and have kids.

Chapter VIII

The Vacation

After the arrest my girls started working in other houses and I was completely alone. Word got out that my place was hot and all the johns were tipped off. Overnight it was as though everyone in the world had dropped off the face of the earth. Everyone that is, except Steve. He called the night after I got out of jail.

"You're the only one who's tried to reach me," I said. Then I realized that he was the only man I knew who wasn't a john.

"What do you mean?" he asked.

"I'll tell you some other time," I said.

"Will you see me tonight? Will you go out with me tonight?"

"I'd love to," I said.

An hour later I was sitting in a cocktail lounge with Steve. I told him about the arrest and my night in jail.

"Celeste, I'm sorry for your trouble," he said, "But it's the best thing that could have happened to you."

"You better believe it!" I said. "I was on the verge of cracking up. I couldn't have gone on much longer."

His clear grey eyes searched mine. "I missed you," he said.

"Likewise," I said.

"Will you be my girl now?"

"Okay, for awhile anyhow," I said.

Later when we were in his apartment Steve said, "Celeste, I still want to marry you. If you ever change your mind, just say the word."

"I'll live with you, Steve, but I can't promise to marry you."

"Okay, Baby, we'll take it from there."

The following evening I put all my clothes into the back of my car and told the superintendent I was moving. Then I drove to Steve's apartment building.

Living with Steve was quiet and peaceful and now that the pressure was off, I couldn't get enough rest and sleep. Steve got up at six in the morning and went to work. I slept until noon and in the afternoon I took it easy. When he came home at night we cooked dinner together and stayed up late. Steve was the only normal man I had ever known. For the first time in my life I was with someone who could be counted on, someone who would not hurt me or use me.

When he came home at night Steve said, "How's my baby?" Then he took me in his arms and kissed me. He was so tender, so gentle.

"Steve, I don't understand how you can love me when you know what I am," I said.

"Celeste, I told you right from the start that your past doesn't matter to me, just so you're faithful to me. I don't think you ever believed me."

"It's still hard to believe," I said.

"In time you'll believe me," he said. "The problem with you is that you were never really loved."

"You're right," I said.

Steve's love for me bordered on adoration.

It was a relief to be away from all the degenerates and the junkies I'd known. And not having to worry about being ripped off, not having to worry about cops was like having a thousand pounds taken off my back. I didn't miss the drinking, the partying and late hours. The only thing that disturbed my peace was the nagging thought of how I was going to make money again. There was no job that paid anything.

Steve and I had been together one month when I had to go to trial. Mr. Weinstein and I sat in the courtroom all morning. My case was called next to last. The trial began and finally the assistant D.A., Mr. Fury, called Sergeant Jack Duffy to the stand.

After Sgt. Duffy took the oath, Mr. Fury said, "Will you please tell the court what happened on the night of February 13?"

"I called Celeste Clemente at 8 p.m. and asked her to meet me at the Park Sheraton Hotel that night at eleven o'clock for the purpose of prostitution. I asked her to bring another girl and I said I would pay them $400. She and Wendy Liebowitz came to the hotel. Celeste, Wendy, Sergeant O'Connor and myself were in room 8928 for almost one hour when I told her I wanted to pay her. I gave her $400 in marked bills. After she put the money in her bag, I pulled out my badge, identified myself as a police officer and placed them under arrest."

"You may step down, Sergeant Duffy," Mr. Fury said.

Mr. Weinstein asked me to take the stand. I took the oath and sat down.

"Miss. Clemente, will you tell the court what happened on the night of February 13?" Mr. Weinstein asked.

"I received a telephone call from a man who said his name was Jack Duffy. He said that a friend of mine had given him my telephone number. That is the only reason I consented to see him," I said. "He asked me to go out to dinner at the Twenty-One Club that night and he asked me to bring a girl friend for a friend of his," I lied. "He asked me to meet him in his room at the Park Sheraton Hotel first. When I arrived at his hotel room with Wendy, we were arrested the minute we walked in the door."

"You may step down," Mr. Weinstein said.

I went back to the witness table and sat down.

"This court finds the defendant, Celeste Clemente, guilty of loitering for the purposes of prostitution and of procuring," Judge Abromowitz said. "Sentencing April 17 at 9:30 a.m. Bail continued. Next case."

We left the courtroom and in the hallway, Mr. Weinstein said, "Don't worry, Celeste. You will receive a suspended sentence on both counts because you have a clean record. But if it ever happens again, that's another story."

"I'm not going to relax until this case is over," I said.

That night when Steve came home, I fell into his arms. "Oh, it's almost over, Steve," I said. "My attorney says I'll get a suspended sentence on both counts next month and that will be the end of it."

"Good, I'm glad, Baby. Then we can relax and settle down."

"I don't know why I ever got into pros in the first place," I said. "That's not true," I added. "I got into it for the money. I made more money in those six months than most men earn in five years. The easy money is what kept me at it. I've got enough stashed away to last me a few years."

"Do you think I love you for your money?" He was teasing.

"You're the only man in the world whose love I could never doubt," I said.

"I told you you'd believe my love was real," he said. "Celeste, let's get engaged." His clear grey eyes held mine.

"Okay," I said. "Why not?"

That Saturday night Steve put a diamond ring on my finger. It was a small stone, but it was beautiful.

Now that I was feeling better, I was haunted more and

more by the fear of how I was going to make money. I could never go back to teaching dancing. Sixty dollars a week would just pay for rent and food. And since I had my energy back I began to feel restless. At first it had been a relief to get away from all the pressures, all the running and the partying. But now I missed the excitement of the old life. I missed wearing beautiful clothes and going to the best clubs in town. I missed getting high. And Steve was a let down. He had no drive. He was too easy going and being with him night after night was beginning to be a bore.

One evening when we were sitting in the living room talking, Steve smiled at me. "Hey, Baby, how about buying me a Corvette?" he asked.

His eyes held mine for a long minute and although he was still smiling, I knew he wasn't joking.

"I'll think about it," I said. His question really turned me off.

As the days passed I resented playing housewife to Steve. I realized that I had never really loved him. I'd been carried away by his goodness and kindness. If I hadn't gotten busted I never would have become involved with him.

Unknown to Steve, I began to make plans. If I received a suspended sentence, I would go to California for a vacation. I knew of a good plastic surgeon in Los Angeles and for a long time I'd wanted another operation on my nose. The first one, done eight years ago, had made a dramatic change in my appearance but now I wanted perfect beauty.

Finally the date for sentencing rolled around. I was so nervous about this court appearance that I took two librium capsules before I left the apartment. I vowed if I got a suspended sentence I would go straight for the rest of my life. I met Mr. Weinstein in the courthouse at nine o'clock. We waited in the courtroom as one case after the other went before the judge. My case was finally called.

"Celeste Clemente, are you ready for sentencing?" the judge asked.

"Yes, your honor," I said.

"Is there anything you would like to say before this court passes sentence on you?"

"Yes, your honor. I am innocent."

"This court sentences you to sixty days on the charge of prostitution and one year on the charge of procuring," he said. "Both sentences to run concurrently, and both are suspended."

I almost jumped for joy!

As I was leaving the courtroom I prayed silently. "Thank you, dear God," I said, "for sparing me and my family."

I was through with my old way of life. A whole new world was waiting for me. A world full of promise, and love and security.

When Steve came home that night we went to a seafood restaurant to celebrate the good news.

"I'm the luckiest girl in the world!" I said. "I came so close to ruining my family. It's almost as if God let me get busted during that newspaper strike so that I could get out of that life without anyone being hurt."

"I feel we're both lucky," Steve said. "If you hadn't gotten busted, I never would have had a chance with you."

Back in the apartment Steve took me in his arms. "Celeste, now we're going to get married. There's no more reason to delay."

I backed away from him and looked into those clear, honest eyes. I had to tell him the truth.

"Steve, I'm sorry but I can't marry you," I said. "I don't know what went wrong. I really thought I loved you but somehow. . . ."

He was incredulous. I couldn't look into his eyes and ran to the bedroom. I heard the door to the apartment close.

Steve had left.

I wrote a note, telling him I was going to a hotel and would pick up my clothes when I found an apartment. I took a few cocktail dresses, some sports clothes, a spring coat and shoes and drove into Manhattan and checked into a hotel. The next afternoon I made an appointment with the plastic surgeon in L.A. for the following Friday. Then I made a reservation for a flight for the next afternoon. Now that I knew I'd be leaving New York for a while, I felt better. Still, I had to live through the night and the thought of being alone unnerved me. I decided to call Frank. For the past seven months he'd never been out of my mind for long. Maybe, just maybe, he would see me.

When he heard my voice he was amazed. "Celeste, I don't believe it! How have you been, Chiquita?"

I had never expected such warmth. "I'm just fine," I said. "How are you, Frank?"

"Do you know what your voice is doing to me?" he asked. "When am I going to see you?"

"Tonight," I said. "Tomorrow I'm flying to the coast."

"Wonderful!" he said. "You can tell me about your trip later. Meet me at our old haunt, the Polynesian Club, at eleven. I'll leave work early and we can spend the rest of the night together."

The rest of the night together! I couldn't believe it.

Early that evening I had my hair done. That night I put on a low-cut red sequined dress. The diamond necklace from Tony was the finishing touch. When I entered the club, Frank came over to me, his eyes flashing.

"Celeste, you never looked more beautiful!" he said, taking my hand.

Once again, after all those months, I was completely hypnotized by Frank.

"You're as handsome as ever," I said, trying to hide my excitement.

He kissed me lightly on the cheek and whispered, "I

could make love to you right now, carino mio."

We sat at a table away from the other patrons. I wondered what had happened in his life to make him change so.

Immediately Frank began telling me everything on his mind.

I made a mistake," he said, "marrying Roberta. She is a, a...disappointment."

I said nothing and he went on. "We're going to have a baby in a few months. I've messed up my life with two bad marriages and pretty soon I'll have two children."

"What are you going to do about it?" I asked.

"I have decided to stick it out with her," he said.

I didn't care if he was happily married or unhappily married. I still wanted him and I'd have him on any terms.

"What about you, Celeste? Why are you leaving town just when I'd like to see you again?"

"I have to get away from the whole scene in New York," I said.

I told him about the arrest. He'd known months ago that I'd gotten into prostitution. I had told Lynn and Ernie and they had wasted no time in telling Frank. They wanted to hurt him for all he'd done to me, but I knew that Frank could not be hurt.

"I'm sorry for your problems," he said.

"I'm glad I'm out of that life," I said. "I can use the vacation and while I'm in Los Angeles, I'm going to have another nose job. I know of a very good plastic surgeon there."

"Well, if you must go, look up my brother Carl. He's just a kid, twenty-one years old, but you'll like him. He goes to college part-time and works as a waiter part-time."

He gave me his brother's address and telephone number at work. Then he said, "Let's get out of here."

We went to my hotel room and after Frank fell asleep, I became depressed. He could never love me as much as I loved him. There was something terribly wrong with Frank. He could never love anyone. I wondered if there was a man anywhere in the world I could love, and who would love me. There was something wrong, something lacking in every relationship.

Late the next afternoon I landed in L.A. and checked into the Beverly Wilshire Hotel in Hollywood. Late that night I reached Carl and made arrangements to meet him at 2:30 a.m. in the lounge of my hotel. When he walked into the lounge I recognized him immediately. He wasn't as good looking as Frank, but he had the same quick, graceful walk. We took a table and I could see he was a little nervous. I told him I was a friend of Frank's and he was pleased.

"Frank is my only relative in this country," he said, "and I haven't seen him for a year. How is he?"

"Frank is fine," I said. "He is doing very well and hopes to become the owner of a restaurant in New York soon."

"I'm happy for him," Carl said. "When I'm finished college I hope to go to New York."

Carl was a nice kid and I knew he didn't have any money. I paid for our drinks and said, "How would you like to go to a night club?"

He grinned. "That would be a nice treat," he said.

We went to a beautiful club and Carl was impressed with the way I spent money.

"One reason I came to L.A. is to have an operation," I said.

"I am so sorry," he said.

"Oh, it's nothing," I said. "I'm not sick. I'm going to have plastic surgery on my nose."

"If I can be of any help, Celeste, just tell me," he said.

"The only hard part is being alone," I said. "Ever since I was a kid, I've dreaded being alone. Even for one night."

He looked at me sympathetically. He didn't understand

that I was extending an invitation.

"Carl, if you live with me until I have recovered from the surgery, I will pay all the bills," I said.

He looked surprised. "I thought you were Frank's girl friend."

"Oh, no," I said. "That was a long time ago."

"Then I'll be glad to stay with you," he said. "I can be your nurse."

The next day we found an apartment and moved in. Two days later I had surgery. When I was back in the apartment Carl took care of everything, waiting on me, shopping and bringing in meals. I felt fine but I had to keep the bandages on for two weeks. I stayed indoors all the time and the days dragged. As each day passed I became more concerned about how I was going to make money. I'd become so accustomed to big money, I couldn't imagine what I would do without it.

At the end of the two weeks the doctor removed the bandages. "A work of art!" he said, holding a mirror up to my face.

"Oh, I like it!" I said. My nose was shorter and smaller and now I was more beautiful than before.

When Carl saw me that night he said, "Celeste, you could be a movie star!"

I laughed. "Carl, tomorrow I'm going to Acapulco," I said. "I really appreciate everything you did for me."

"I was glad to help," he said. "When you see Frank, ask him to visit me."

When I landed in Acapulco I was overwhelmed by the tropical beauty. Everywhere I looked there were palm trees. Light blue waters shimmered under a cloudless sky. I checked into the Hilton Hotel, put on my bathing suit and beach robe, and went down to the pool. When the waiter came by I ordered a Pina Colada. I took off my robe and sat on a lounge chair. I wasn't there ten minutes when a man stopped in front of me. He was in his thirties and very attractive. "Mind if I sit down?" he asked.

"Okay," I said.

"My name is Ron Newhouse," he said. "I'm here for a couple of weeks."

"I'm Celeste," I said.

"I'm a pilot with the airlines," he said. "Would you care to have dinner with me tonight?"

"I'm busy," I said.

"That's too bad," he said. "I was hoping to find company for the evening."

"I'm on vacation," I said. "A vacation from men."

He laughed. "I'll buy you the biggest lobster in Acapulco."

"It just happens lobster is my favorite food," I said.

"Good. Eight o'clock, okay?"

"Fine," I said.

"I have two buddies who are looking for dates. Do you know any girls here?"

"No," I said. "I just arrived."

"See you at eight, Celeste," he said and walked off toward the hotel.

A few minutes later two attractive girls came into the pool area. They were both tall and slender and had the same shining black hair. I smiled at them and they took chairs next to mine. We introduced ourselves. Gail and Cindy had deep blue eyes with thick, dark lashes.

"Does everyone ask if you're twins?"

They laughed. "Everyone," Cindy said.

"We're just sisters," Gail said.

They ordered drinks and Cindy said, "Do you want to have dinner with us?"

"I have a date," I said, "but if you girls don't have anything to do, my date knows a couple of guys looking for girls."

"Is there any money involved?" Gail asked.

I laughed. "I'm a prostitute too, but I didn't let on to

my date."

"Small world," Cindy said. "Ask him if there's any money involved. If there is, then we would be interested."

I left a message for Ron with the switchboard operator and an hour later he came back to the pool. I introduced him to the girls.

He smiled. "Would you girls like to go out for dinner?"

Gail and Cindy nodded.

"Terrific!" Ron said. "I'll tell Ned and Burke."

"If your friends want action," I said, "these girls want $100 each."

"No problem," he said and left.

Gail and Cindy told me they'd been in Acapulco for three months, working out of the better hotels. As we talked, the fears I'd had after my arrest vanished. The promise I'd made to myself never to go back into prostitution somehow didn't seem important anymore. I realized now that the only real fear I'd had during the past two months was the fear of not making money. I had been preoccupied with the thought of how I was going to make big money. Here was the answer. Prostitution was the only way for me.

I started working that night and for the next couple of weeks I got johns through the maitres d' of various hotels. Then one day I thought, "This is ridiculous! If I'm doing it here, I might as well go back to New York and do it there, where the action is, where the money is."

Chapter IX

Back in Business

I found a luxurious, spacious three-bedroom apartment in an exclusive neighborhood, part of a complex of four buildings. It was on the sixteenth floor and off the living room was a terrace overlooking a garden. Fountains, statues and benches were encircled by tall hedges. With new carpeting, draperies, furniture and oil paintings, it was the most lavish apartment I had ever seen.

I contacted Melanie and Lana and just before they were due to come over, I had to go to the bank. When I walked out of the elevator, a tall, good-looking airline pilot was standing in the lobby. He smiled when he saw me.

"You're going out and I'm coming in," he said. "What a shame."

I smiled briefly and started toward the doorway. He blocked me and said, "I'm Brian McFadden. I live in apartment 15 D."

"I'm Celeste," I said, trying to walk past him. He stepped in front of me again.

"It's not every day I meet such a beautiful girl," he said.

He had beautiful big blue eyes and it was obvious he could have any girl he wanted.

"Could I buy you a drink?"

"I'm afraid not," I said. "I have a jealous boyfriend."

I brushed past him and went out the door.

When Melanie and Lana walked into the apartment, they let out cries of delight.

"Wow, this place is first class!" Lana said. "Sweetie, we missed you!" She kissed me. "It's good to have you back where you belong."

Melanie was thinner but as beautiful as ever. She hugged me. "I'm so glad you're back, Celeste," she said. "I could not have gone on much longer working in that other house."

I was touched by her love and dependence but I was concerned. "Honey, we have to fatten you up a little," I said. "You've gotten too thin."

"It was a long time, almost three months," she said. "There was nothing to do, nowhere to go except visit my brother in the rehab center. Dick got busted again but this time he had the best lawyer in New York and instead of sending him to prison again, the judge sent him to this rehab place."

I'd heard about her brother. He was a notorious drug dealer and had been convicted and imprisoned three years ago. Then last year his case had been appealed and he'd won and walked out a free man. There had been an outrage in the press.

"Next Sunday, Melanie, you're going with me to my mother's for dinner."

She smiled. "I'd love to," she said.

After we talked for awhile I said, "From now on girls, we aren't taking any chances. I have devised a code system for our johns and no one is getting in here without giving his code number."

"Sounds like a cloak and dagger arrangement," Lana said.

I reached into my pocketbook and pulled out a sheet of paper. "Here it is," I said, pushing the paper across the table for them to study. "In the first column you will see numbers with fractions. Only the fraction is significant and it means money. Half means $50; 3/4 means $75; 4/4 means $100. In the second column you'll notice there are single capital letters. These designate a john's preference. *S* means straight; *T* means two girls; *G* means another guy; and *O* is for orgy. In the third column is the name of the john. The fourth column is his address and the fifth column is his telephone number. The numbers in these two columns are to be read backwards. In the sixth column is the john's code number."

"Celeste, you are a genius!" Lana said. "You should be working for the FBI." And she hit the table and started laughing.

"The pay is better here," I said. "Seriously, girls, from now on I take all calls, without one exception. And when I'm not here the place is frozen. When a john calls he must give his name and identify himself with his code number. My girls may not make dates on the outside through any recommendations. Every john you meet on the outside has to be someone I know. To further insure our security I have paid off the doorman. Before a john or a girl comes up here, first they have to call on the intercom from the lobby."

"It's foolproof!" Melanie said.

"It will be impossible for the police to break this code," I said. "I'll never get busted again."

I contacted my other girls and started calling the johns.

"Celeste!" George Woodlawn said when he heard my voice, "am I glad you're back in town!"

"Back in business, George!" I laughed.

"There's no place like yours," he said. "The rest of these houses are just cut and dried, hit and run. In your place I can sit down and enjoy myself."

Word spread like wildfire and in less than a week the four phones were ringing night and day. Every john we'd ever known was calling and asking to bring over new johns. All my old girls were back.

The first time Renee walked into the apartment I was shocked. Instead of the statuesque redhead of three months ago, she was now so thin her shoulder blades were protruding.

"What happened to you?" I asked, but I already knew.

"I lost a little weight," she said.

"A little! Like twenty pounds!" I said. "Renee, before it's too late, please go to the hospital and kick your habit."

"My face is still all right," she said.

"Yes, your face is beautiful, but in this business your figure has to be beautiful too," I said. "I can count your ribs from here."

"She'll never need an X-ray," Lana said.

"You know I could never kick my habit, Celeste," she said.

"In another month I won't be able to use you," I said. She knew I was serious.

"Okay, I'll try. I'll go to the hospital," she said.

I made the necessary arrangements and that afternoon, before she could change her mind, Renee was driven by Tracy to an upstate hospital that treated junkies with medication so they could withdraw.

After they'd left I said to Melanie and Lana, "You should both go to the hospital before it's too late." Then I told them about the junkies I'd seen in the jail.

"I'm not worried," Lana said. "I'm happy the way I am."

"If I couldn't get high, I couldn't go on living," Melanie said.

The doorbell rang.

"Now, who could that be?" Melanie asked.

"I'm not expecting a john for an hour," I said. I got up and walked to the door and looked through the peephole. It was Brian. I opened the door slightly.

"Celeste!" He was smiling.

"Brian, I told you before I have a jealous boyfriend. Now please don't come here again."

"Wouldn't you let me take you out for one drink?"

"I'm sorry, Brian. The answer is no."

"Well, you can't blame me for trying," he said.

I said good bye and closed the door. "That guy is a real pest," I said.

"That's the price you pay for being so gorgeous!" Lana laughed.

I was relieved when I got up Sunday afternoon. When I went home, I could relax and forget. All week Melanie had been looking forward to spending Sunday at my home. When she was showered and dressed I said, "We'll be leaving in a few minutes."

She looked at me nervously. "I'm sorry, Celeste, I can't go."

"Why not?"

"I'm getting sick," she said. "I have to go to New York."

"Melanie, you cannot work for me any longer if you go on shooting stuff," I said.

Her eyes widened in disbelief. I realized that by mothering her all these months I'd been giving in to her, making it easier for her to stay hooked.

"Oh, Celeste, you don't mean that!" she cried.

"Oh yes I do!" I said. "Melanie, I am not only thinking of my business, I am thinking of your welfare."

"But you know. . . ."

I wouldn't let her finish. "Melanie, I've known you for eight months and in that time you have been shooting more and more. It has got to stop."

"All right," she said. "I'll try to kick."

"I'm not fooling, honey. Either you kick your habit or you find another house to work in."

"Celeste, I'll do it. I swear I'll do it!"

"Okay. Today you take a cab to Manhattan and get your fix, but when I'm back here tomorrow afternoon, we'll get the medication from Dr. Bolan and you'll kick right here in the apartment."

"Okay, tomorrow. I promise."

When I came back Monday afternoon Melanie opened the door for me.

"I haven't had a fix since last night," she said.

"Good. Now don't panic," I said. "Dr. Bolan told me long ago he would furnish medication for any girls who want to detox."

I sent Lana to the doctor's office and she returned an hour later with the medication. It was now 3 p.m. and Melanie was beginning to sweat. I gave her the bottle of pills.

"Don't down them all, Melanie. Take them when you need them, according to directions."

She took two pills and about twenty minutes later she began to feel better.

"Maybe it's going to work," she said.

"It's got to work! No matter how you feel later, just make up your mind you're going through with it."

In another couple of hours Melanie was sweating and feeling sick. A couple of johns were in the bedrooms and Melanie began crying.

"You better go in the bathroom and close the door," I said.

A few hours later Melanie had severe cramps and was sick to her stomach. She was crying and cursing. "Oh, God, Celeste, I can't stand it! The pills aren't helping at all!"

"You've got to live through it," I said. I was not going to give in to her. She was too dear to me and I didn't want anything to happen to her. I was afraid if she stayed on the junk she wasn't going to last long.

An hour later we had our last john over for the evening. While he was in a bedroom, Melanie was in the bathroom crying brokenly. I went to the bathroom and said, "We have a john here, Melanie." But it was pointless to say anything. I could tell by her face she wasn't going to make it. She doubled over with cramps and began calling on God to take her. I closed the door and went back to the living room.

When the john was leaving later he said, "Celeste, if you're going to use junkies, you're going to lose customers."

He was right. I took Lana aside. "Get your works together fast and I'll ask Etran to take Melanie down to the garage."

Lana ran out the door and two minutes later Etran and Melanie left. When the girls returned a few minutes later, Melanie was fine. She came over to me but she was afraid to say anything.

"I'm not going to throw you out," I said. "If it was anyone else, I would. But not you, Melanie."

Tears rushed to her eyes. "Oh, thank you, Celeste," she said. "You're the best friend I ever had in my life."

A few days later Tracy returned from visiting Renee in the hospital.

"Well, how's Renee?" I asked.

"She wasn't there," Tracy said. "That twenty dollars you sent her for cigarettes and snacks she used to buy some coke. Her roommate told me as soon as she got the money she checked out and no one's seen her since."

"Well, that's the end of her," I said. "She wouldn't have the nerve to come back here now."

Business was booming and I could be even more particular about my girls. I started turning down girls. I refused to take any more junkies. The stakes were too high and I was through taking unnecessary risks.

I was getting all kinds of johns, straight and freaky. Harry was one of the straightest guys I'd ever met. He was an accountant, soft spoken, low key. The first time he came over he asked me for a cup of coffee before he went in with one of the girls. After that the cup of coffee became a routine. I soon realized the coffee was just an excuse for him to talk. Harry was married, starved for sex and starved for conversation.

"Yours is the first house I've been to," he said a few weeks later. "And since I started coming here, I can't stay away."

Harry came over once a week, same day, same time, like clockwork. One time he said, "Celeste, would you consider cooking dinner for me once a week?"

I laughed. I had a problem with him as it was. After he had a girl he always wanted to sit and talk to me and would have stayed for hours if I didn't ask him to leave.

One afternoon a man called. "Celeste, this is Bill Piedmont," he said. "I got your number from Jack Sherman and I'd like to come over."

Jack was a nice guy, but he knew the rules. A new john had to be brought over personally by a john already known to me. Of course, it was just as likely this Bill Piedmont was a cop, posing as a john.

"You tell Jack Sherman to bring you up here himself," I said and hung up.

D. J. Cromarity, an assemblyman called one day. "Celeste, a friend of mine is an assistant district attorney. He's a great guy and wants to meet you."

I laughed. "Okay, bring him over," I said.

When I told the girls an assistant D.A. was on the way over they laughed.

"I'll bet," Lana said. "He's probably working for the Mob."

When they arrived D.J. introduced us. "Celeste, this is Roland Barbaro," he said.

Roland shook my hand and his quick, dark eyes roamed over the apartment, taking in everything.

"This is a nice place you have," he said, inspecting one of the oil paintings. He was not a good looking man but he was intelligent looking. He had dark hair and a protruding nose. I introduced him to the girls. Lana could hardly keep a straight face and I hoped she was not going to make a crack. Roland looked each girl over carefully.

"Girls, you don't have a thing to worry about," he said. "I work out of the D.A.'s office and I like to have my fun."

He had a stacatto way of speaking. Maybe that was what I didn't like about him. "Which girl would you like?" I asked.

"Tracy," he said. "I'll have her today."

After he left Lana said, "If he works for the D.A., then I work for the New York Public Library."

"Until you can prove otherwise," I said, "treat him with respect."

Another john was Ross Baker, a handsome business tycoon in his late forties. When he came over he said, "Celeste, I like young girls. When you get an eighteen-year-old with blue eyes and red hair, call me. But," he added, "she must have chubby arms and legs."

I laughed. "Will do," I said.

When I found a girl who fitted his description, I called him and he sent his chauffered limousine for her. Ross kept a suite of rooms at the Commodore Hotel on a year-round basis for his extra marital affairs with call girls.

Another time he called. "Celeste, I want an eighteen-year-old with brown eyes and long, blond hair. And don't forget the chubby arms and legs."

"I'll put your order in," I said.

I was getting the same strange story back from every girl I sent to Ross.

"Celeste, Ross Baker is a real freak scene!" Linda, the brown eyed blond said. "First he lectured me. He said, 'Young lady, you should not be doing this and you know it. It is not right. It is not normal. And you could pick up a disease.'" She giggled. "Then he said, 'Linda, are you ready to make love?' "

Occasionally Ross took me out for dinner. The reason I

like you so much, Celeste," he said one night, "is because you make me laugh."

"That's a talent I've had for a long time," I said.

Ross was always keyed up and bursting with ideas for making money. "We're putting up a mall on Long Island that will revolutionize shopping centers," he said. He went on to describe the architecture, the walks with benches and small pools.

"It sounds fabulous," I said.

Before we finished the meal he said, "Celeste, I'm looking for an eighteen-year-old with brown eyes and short curly black hair. And don't forget the arms and legs."

I laughed. What the hell, I thought. If he has the money he can order whatever he wants.

The following night Tony and Victor came over for one of our steak dinners. About ten o'clock the doorbell rang. Tony gave me a surprised look. "Don't worry," I said. "I know who it is. He's a pest but he's harmless."

I went to the door and looked through the peephole. It was Brian. "Yes, Brian," I said, opening the door slightly.

"Celeste, I'm giving a party and I want you to come downstairs." He'd had too much to drink.

"Brian, I cannot go to your apartment," I said firmly. "Now please leave."

"Celeste, I've got a big crowd over and everyone wants to meet you."

"I am not going to your party, Brian. Now please leave and don't come back."

"God damn it!" he said. "What do I have to do to get you in my apartment?"

Instantly Tony was at my side and before I knew what had happened, he had pulled out a knife and was cutting into Brian's arm. Blood was spurting and as I stood there frozen, Tony kept on cutting deeper and deeper. Brian doubled over and now Victor was on the other side of me quietly cutting into Brian's other arm. Blood was on the floor, the wall, and the doorway and not one word had been spoken. Finally Brian broke away and ran to the elevator. I was terrified the police would be called and my business discovered, and this time it would mean prison. Within the next two minutes Tony and Victor had washed all the blood away and the four of us were downstairs and outside in Tony's cadillac, driving to Manhattan.

Now everything fitted together. The fawning over Tony in the restaurant, the fear his presence engendered in the patrons there, the hot mink coat, the. diamond necklace, the watch from Tiffany's. Of course, he didn't make all that money from the car wash. That was just a front.

"You're working for the Mob," I said. "All this time you've been working for the Mob and I didn't know it."

"You read too many detective stories, Celeste," he said.

Later when the four of us were in a nightclub, Tony excused himself for a few minutes. And Victor said to me in a lowered voice, "Celeste, you're a very lucky girl that Tony didn't kill that guy. He's a big man in the Mob. As a matter of fact, he's number one man on the lower east side."

"My God!" I said.

The next day I cancelled all appointments for the next few days. I didn't know if Brian had talked to the police or if the doctors had reported it. After several days went by and nothing happened, I began to breathe easier. A week after the incident while I was in the lobby one evening waiting for the elevator, Brian walked into the building.

"Good evening, Celeste," he said. The burning invitation in his eyes was gone and in its place was respect.

"Hello," I said.

From that time on all the tenants in the building treated me with exaggerated courtesy. They were actually afraid of me. Later I learned from the doorman they thought I was working with the Mafia.

Chapter X

The Pot of Gold

Dawn, a new girl, came over one afternoon. After I explained the house rules to her, she smiled. "Celeste, you have to meet Allison," she said. "She has been looking for someone like you for a long time."

"What do you mean?" I asked.

"She's been looking for a high class call girl for a very high class guy."

"I already have customers from the very elite," I said.

"Allison was seeing a multi-millionaire and something went wrong. Ever since she's been looking for someone in our business for him" Dawn said.

"Who is he?" I asked.

"Peter Finchley," she said.

"Peter Finchley!" I gasped. "I can't believe it!"

Peter Finchley was a name known all over America. All over the world. "When can I meet Allison?" I asked.

Dawn set up an appointment for me and a few days later I went to Allison's apartment. Allison was a striking brunette with deep-set blue eyes and an ivory complexion.

"Celeste, I hope you're the one," she said, looking me over carefully. She mixed drinks for us. "I'd still be seeing Peter but I made a mistake," she said, "a big mistake."

She smiled suddenly. "But someone else will benefit from my mistake."

"What was the mistake?" I asked.

She disregarded my question and I realized she was not going to tolerate any interruptions. "How long have you been in this racket?" she asked.

"I started over nine months ago," I said.

"What did you do before that?"

"I was an instructor at a dance studio," I said.

"Are you hooked on anything?"

"No, thank God."

She kept on questioning me, searching and probing. "Dawn was right about you, Celeste," she said. "You're not only beautiful, you're intelligent and that counts just as much as looks with Peter."

"Thank you," I said.

"Peter will like you," she said.

"He sounds very interesting," I said, laughing.

"A lot of girls would like to meet Peter," Allison said, "but believe me, Peter would not like to meet most of them. Peter cannot bear stupid women. And I think you'll agree most of the girls we know are not too bright."

"I know what you mean," I said.

She questioned me further about my business and the problems with my girls, then said, "I'm glad you're not one of those poor-little-me girls, always sniffling about her unhappy childhood."

I laughed. "I've never told my troubles to my johns or my girls. It would scare the johns away, and the girls need someone to lean on."

"Good," she said. "Peter needs a girl with a strong personality. Celeste, Peter would like you. You are the one!" She smiled triumphantly and I wondered why she was so pleased.

"I saw Peter for several months, which is quite a record," she said. "I made up my mind that I was going to keep him and I might have but I made a mistake. I stole money from him. He dropped me and ever since I've been looking for someone for him, someone in our business. I can't see all that money going to some dame in the circles he travels in."

"I don't understand what you're getting at," I said.

She leaned forward. "What I'm saying, Celeste, is that if you play your cards right, he's yours. And I'm not talking about prostituting. I'm talking about marriage!"

"Marriage!" I was incredulous.

"I'm serious," Allison said. "Peter desperately wants to be married. The only thing in this world he wants is love. The love of one woman. He's not a philanderer at heart. He is a terribly lonely man who would lay down his life for a woman he believed really loved him."

"What makes you think he would want to marry me?" I asked.

"I know Peter. I know what he likes and what he needs. He wants a woman that number one is a beautiful female animal; number two is intelligent; and number three is strong, someone he can lean on, someone who can understand and put up with him."

"Put up with him?"

"Peter has his eccentricities," Allison smiled strangely. "But with all his millions, it shouldn't be too difficult to tolerate him."

"It sounds unbelievable," I said.

"It's not," she said. Then in a lowered voice she said, "Celeste, you don't have to go on forever doing what you're doing. You can have the biggest money in the world with one man legitimately. You may even get to like him."

"I'm intrigued," I said.

Allison smiled. 'We're going to go about this very carefully. I want you to come over here a couple of hours a day for about a week and I'll tell you everything there is to know about Peter—his likes, his dislikes, his personal habits, his prejudices, his family background, everything. Then when you meet him, you'll know exactly how to act, exactly what to say and what not to say."

The following afternoon I went back to see Allison.

"You can understand that Peter thinks every woman is after his money," she said. "The point is never to accept money from him. This is a cardinal rule. And he will keep pushing it on you. Just keep refusing it. Always act as if you don't want anything from him. This will take some convincing. But once you've convinced him you're not interested in his money, you will be different from every other female on earth. And that's your starting point."

"That makes sense," I said.

"You have to understand Peter's family to understand why he behaves the way he does," she said. "His father left his mother when Peter was three years old. He never saw his father again. His mother was an alcoholic and Peter was brought up by servants mostly. His mother has been in a sanitarium for years. He has an older sister whom he despises because his father took an interest in her. The sister was invited to the father's home regularly but for some reason the father didn't want to see Peter. Anyhow, the result is, naturally, that Peter is a very bitter man. He's been married three times and has four children. He hates his wives and says not one of them ever loved him. They were all after his money. He claims his children are ingrates and just use him for his money. When he goes down the list of people who don't love him, just baby him. Peter is still looking for love, but he is so screwed up he'll never find it."

Allison stood up. "That's all for today. I have to meet a trick."

The next afternoon Allison told me about Peter's wealth and financial background, most of which I already knew. It was part of American folklore.

"Celeste, don't be disturbed if Peter tells you he doesn't

have money. It's just one of his eccentricities. He has days when he really believes he's just an average middle class Joe."

"It must be awful!" I laughed.

"There's one thing I can say for Peter. He's very good to people who work for him. He won't tolerate unkindness or rudeness. One time in his penthouse we were having dinner with a friend of his. The maid spilled some cream and if ran off the tablecloth onto the man's pants. He jumped up and started cursing at the maid. Peter threw him out and told him never to come back.

Allison recounted story after story so that I would never offend Peter. "Remember, his problems are the worst," she said. "No one else is allowed to have problems. It would never cross Peter's mind that possibly he could be at fault."

"He sounds very self-centered," I said.

"As self-centered as a baby in a crib," she said. "By the way, Peter hates Jews. Never wear furs or jewelry. They remind him of a Jew. His taste is quiet, unobtrusive. Keep your clothes simple. No beaded gowns, no bright colors, no decolletage and no diamonds. A single strand of cultured pearls is all that Peter can tolerate."

I saw Allison a few more times. The last time she went over everything. I felt like a kid in school preparing for an examination.

"Celeste, be hard to get," she said. "And any time Peter's idiosyncracies get to you, just think of that pot of gold."

I got up to leave. "Thanks, Allison," I said. "I'll keep you posted."

"Celeste, you can do it!" she said. "You can become Mrs. Peter Finchley and all the girls in the Four Hundred Club will have to cry their eyes out!" I laughed.

"And remember, by the time you're forty-five, he'll be an old man. With a little luck, you'll be a widow before you're fifty!"

Allison made arrangements for me to meet Peter on a Tuesday afternoon at 4 p.m. in his penthouse. I wore a simple white silk dress and no jewelry at all. For the occasion I had bought a black broadcloth coat.

When I rang the bell the houseboy opened the door. I gave my name.

"You'll find Mr. Finchley in there," the boy said, pointing to a doorway across the foyer.

I opened the door and there was Peter lying in bed with two young girls.

"You must be Celeste!" he said, smiling.

"I'm insulted!" I cried. "You were expecting me and this is how I meet you?"

I turned and walked back to the foyer, ignoring his apologies. Before I could reach the outer door, he was standing behind me in a robe.

"Celeste, please forgive me. I'm really sorry. I'll get rid of the girls. Please stay!"

I turned around and glared at him. "I wouldn't think of staying here," I said. "I don't have to put up with this!"

He begged me not to leave. There was such a childlike pleading in his eyes that I could not walk out. I sat down on a chair in the foyer and he went back to the bedroom. Within two minutes the girls had left. The houseboy brought in a tray with several brands of Scotch and a bucket of ice, a glass and water and soda.

"I don't care for a drink, thank you," I said.

When Peter reappeared about twenty minutes later, he was dressed in a navy pin-striped suit, white shirt and dark tie. He came over to me, his blue eyes wide and expressive.

"Celeste, I am so sorry." He took my hands in his. "Now we shall start all over again and you'll see I can be quite nice."

"All right," I said.

"You are more beautiful than Allison told me," he said.

"Thank you," I said.

"Why aren't you drinking?" he asked.

"I don't want a drink," I said. "Later, perhaps."

Peter did not like women who guzzled highballs.

He took my hand and we walked into the living room.

"You take that chair," he said, "and I'll sit over here where I can see you to best advantage."

Peter was not a good looking man, but he had beautiful eyes. He was about five feet eight inches tall and grossly overweight. He must have weighed 250 pounds.

"Celeste, your figure is exquisite!" he said.

"Thank you," I said and smiled.

"And that smile is devastating!"

He went to the sideboard and started mixing drinks. "What would you like?" he asked.

"A Chivas Regal and water," I said.

"I see you have good taste in Scotch as well as in clothes," he said.

He sat down and as we talked he studied me. I'd never had a man look at me so intently. "You wouldn't mind having dinner here in my penthouse next time, would you?" he asked. "I don't care to eat in restaurants. I don't like people pointing me out."

"I'd enjoy having dinner with you," I said. "It's the company."

Peter smiled. Then matter-of-factly he said, "I'd like to take you to bed now."

"I'm not ready for that," I said.

"Well, how long would it take you to be ready?"

"I don't just jump into bed with a man I hardly know," I said.

"I'll make it worth your while," he said, walking over to me. "Name your price."

"I don't want any money," I said evenly. "I am not a prostitute."

He persisted but I was adamant.

Later as I was leaving, Peter asked, "May I see you to-morrow evening?"

I knew just what to say. "A week from today," I said.

"A week?"

"A week," I said.

He took down my telephone number. "Next Tuesday at six," he said.

Peter called me three times during the week, asking me to come over but I was firm and did not see him again until Tuesday.

The second time I was more relaxed and confident. Peter was charming and good company. He was quite a raconteur and I appreciated his wit. When we sat down to dinner I couldn't believe the amount of food placed on the table by the maid. "Are you expecting other guests?" I asked.

Peter laughed. "Oh, no. I enjoy eating. Nothing wrong with that, is there?"

"Of course not," I said.

There was a platter of roast beef, bowls of mashed potatoes, peas, asparagus, creamed onions and mushrooms. There was a gravy boat, rolls and butter and a large bowl of salad. Peter poured a red wine into our glasses. I took a serving of roast beef, asparagus, mushrooms and some salad. Peter piled his plate with generous portions of everything, including three rolls. Then he proceeded to devour his dinner, eating as fast as possible and making smacking noises with his mouth. Before I had finished what was on my plate, Peter was helping himself to seconds. In my life I'd never seen anyone eat like that. When he'd finished the second plate, he leaned back in his chair, placed his hand on his stomach and let out a loud, resounding burp. I was shocked. I stared at him but he was completely oblivious to my reaction. He rang for the maid.

"More of everything, please, Gertrude," he said.

The maid removed everything from the table and set our places again. The kitchen help must have anticipated his need because he didn't have to wait two minutes when bowls of vegetables, a platter of beef and another salad were brought in.

"Celeste, would you care for a little more?" Peter asked.

I forced a smile. "No thank you," I said.

Anytime Peter's idiosyncracies get to you, just think of that pot of gold, Allison had said. I could not look at Peter as he attacked the food and instead I kept staring at the centerpiece, a crystal bowl filled with pink and white carnations. Several minutes passed and then Peter let out another long and loud burp. He had made no effort to control the burp but, like a small boy, had deliberately given it all the volume he could.

"More wine?" Peter asked.

"All right," I said.

A minute later the maid was back, clearing the table. Then she brought in a lemon meringue pie and a silver coffee service. I refused the dessert and Peter helped himself to a large piece of pie, then another, and another until the entire pie was gone. I could not believe my eyes.

"Excuse me, Celeste," Peter said, standing. "I'll be back in a few minutes. I have to get rid of all I ate."

This is what those Roman orgies must have been like, I thought.

When Peter returned he sat down as though nothing unusual had taken place. He recounted stories about trips he'd made to the Bahamas, telling me about their tropical fruits and wonderful seafood. An hour must have passed when Peter rang for the maid.

"I'm ready, Gertrude," he said.

A moment later the maid returned with a platter of lamb chops, bowls of creamed carrots, broccoli au gratin, green squash, scalloped potatoes, a bowl of salad and dark bread and butter.

"Could you eat a little more, Celeste?" Peter asked.

"No, thank you," I said pleasantly. "I have to watch

my figure."

"Of course. I understand," he said.

He heaped his plate with large servings of everything and I kept a smile on my face as he washed down the food with wine. He did not eat as fast as he had the first time, but when he was finished he leaned back in his chair again, placed his hand on his stomach and let out that long, resounding burp. "I like to eat," he said. "It's one of the few things in life I really enjoy."

"That's nice," I said.

He helped himself to seconds but this time he did not eat as much. Nor did he have any dessert, just a cup of coffee. And he had no thirds.

When we went into the living room, Peter poured Cherry Heering into cordial glasses. He sat down next to me on the couch and after we'd been talking for a while, he said suddenly, "Celeste, I must have you. Will you go to bed with me now?"

"I'm afraid not," I said.

"I'll give you any amount you want," he said.

"I don't believe in selling my body," I said.

"Well then, how about just for fun?"

"Peter, there's more to going to bed with a man than sex."

"That hasn't been my experience," he said.

"Well, that's unfortunate," I said.

"Will you come over for dinner Friday night?" he asked.

"How about Tuesday, a week from tonight?"

"That's a long time," he said, "but if I can't change your mind, I'll just have to wait."

"You can't change my mind, Peter," I said. "I always mean what I say."

"I'm beginning to believe that," he said. "You are a very strong-willed young woman."

The next time I was with Peter was easier. At least I was prepared for his manner of eating. Whenever it got to be too much I thought of that pot of gold.

After dinner Peter seemed even more eager to please me.

"Celeste, you are so beautiful, so intelligent, and so. . ." His voice faltered. "So unusual that I will do anything for you, just name it."

"There's really nothing you can do for me, Peter," I said.

"Celeste, would you go away with me to Bermuda?"

"I can't," I said. "I have too many things going in New York."

"I don't understand you," he said. "You won't go away with me. You won't go to bed with me. You won't take money from me. What do you want?"

"Peter, the only thing I want is love," I said. "I have been looking for years for one man I could love, one man who could love me and be true to me."

He took both my hands in his. "That is exactly what I have been looking for," he said. "I'm forty-four years old, Celeste, and I haven't found one woman I can love. I haven't found one woman who can love me and be faithful to me."

His eyes filled with tears. Allison was right. He was like a little boy with his desperate need for love. I felt sorry for Peter.

Later when I was leaving, he put his arm around me. "Celeste, you have a pure heart. You're not like all the others. If you change your mind, call me and we'll go to Bermuda."

After that evening our relationship changed. Instead of making him wait a week, I saw Peter two nights later. The better I knew him, the more pity I felt for him. With all his wealth, Peter was the most pathetic man I had ever known. Finally, one night I consented to go to bed with him.

"Celeste, I'm falling for you. I really am," he said. Then he reached for his wallet and handed me a few bills.

"No, Peter. I meant what I said before. I will not take money from you."

He was childishly delighted. "Celeste, I want you over here every night. I cannot live without you."

"You know I can't do that, Peter. I have my own life to lead."

"I can be very jealous," he said.

"There's no one else," I said.

I began to see Peter two and three times a week. Now he was confiding in me, telling me everything that had bothered him since he was a small child.

"My mother was never a mother to me. She was always inebriated. I can't remember my mother being sober."

He told me about his wives and children, his father and sister. It didn't matter which person he was talking about, or which words he used, the message was always the same—Peter had been unloved. As Allison advised, I babied him. The weeks went by and Peter continued to pour out his heart. One evening after he'd gone down the list of people who should have loved him but didn't, he said, "Celeste, believe me when I tell you there isn't a human being on this earth who loves me, who's ever loved me."

There were tears in his eyes. There was something terribly wrong with Peter. It was something deep within Peter himself.

Whenever I was with Peter he told me he loved me. And each time he continued to offer me money. I knew he was testing me, but it was odd he should keep testing me for so long. He'd find out soon enough, I thought. The only way I'd accept money from Peter would be as his wife. The longer I knew him, the more I fantasized about becoming Mrs. Peter Finchley. Everything I'd ever wanted would be mine.

One night Peter said, "You know, Celeste, I realize there are many people who are unhappy. But what is so hard to take is that I am one of the wealthiest men in the world and with all my money I have not been able to buy anything of real value. I know you can't buy love, but you would think I would have found it once. Just once." Then looking into my eyes with that childish, pleading look, he said, "Do you think you could love me?"

"Maybe some day, Peter," I said. "Love is too big a commitment so I won't tell you I love you until I'm sure."

"I appreciate that," he said. "More than you know."

The next time I was with Peter he said, "Celeste, would you go to Bermuda with me now?"

"Yes, Peter," I said. "I'm ready to go away with you."

He took my hand and looked at me with such tenderness. "You have made me very happy," he said.

Bermuda was more beautiful than I had imagined. We had a suite of rooms overlooking the ocean. Our second night there Peter said, "Celeste, I've never loved anyone the way I love you. I want you to marry me."

"I'm not sure it would work for us," I said. I was at the brink now. I had to be very careful. Anything could upset the apple cart, one wrong word or look.

"I know you like me," he said. "And that's enough. I don't ask for the impossible."

"I do like you, Peter," I said.

"Even if you don't love me," he said, "we could be happy together. I know we could."

"Peter, I just can't jump into a marriage," I said.

He let the subject drop.

One night around 1 a.m. we were sitting in our living room. "I'm very hungry," Peter said suddenly. He called room service. "What do you mean room service is closed?" he barked. "I'm hungry!"

There was a pause and then he said, "I don't care how you do it, but I want ten bacon and tomato sandwiches and a pot of coffee. I will pay you $200 for them." Then he hung up.

About forty minutes later the bell boy came in. "Mr. Finchley, your sandwiches are here," he said. "The room clerk found a cab driver whose wife made them for you."

Peter handed the boy two one-hundred dollar bills and then gave him a ten dollar tip.

"Thank you, sir!" The boy grinned.

The next afternoon Peter and I went for a swim in the ocean. When we came out of the water, we walked along the shore and Peter seemed very depressed.

"What's the matter with you today?" I asked.

He took my hand. "Let's sit in the sand," he said.

We sat down and he said, "Celeste, I haven't told you this before, but I'm not really wealthy. Not at all."

"What?" I couldn't believe he was serious.

"I've lost a great deal of money over the years and I'm not the wealthy man you may think I am."

For a moment I was speechless. After listening to his endless conversations about how everyone had been using him for his money all his life, I found this hilariously funny. I was on the point of laughing when I recalled Allison's words: "There are days when he actually believes he's just an average middle-class Joe."

"I'm sorry to hear that, Peter," I said. "It's rough, I know."

His expression never changed and for the rest of the afternoon he talked about his losses in the stock market, his poor business judgment, and how taxes had eaten up much of his fortune.

"Peter has his eccentricities," Allison had said. It was more than that. His eccentricities and idiosyncrasies added together amounted to mental illness.

Peter never stopped asking me to marry him. "You're the only woman who doesn't want anything from me," he said. "I must have you for my wife, Celeste."

"When I'm sure it's right to marry you, I'll tell you," I said.

"I can wait," he said, smiling contentedly.

If I married Peter, I wouldn't have to put up with the freak scenes with the johns and homosexuals. I wouldn't have to hustle for money. I wouldn't have to worry about cops. If I married Peter, the world would be at my feet. So what if I didn't love him? I'd never find a man I could love. Still, strangely, something held me back and I kept putting him off.

Now that marrying Peter was within my grasp, I could think of nothing else. But the more I thought about marrying him, the less the idea appealed to me. It was quite a shock when I realized finally that in spite of all his money and in spite of all my strategy, I could not marry Peter.

Our last night in Bermuda I said to Peter, "I don't want to hurt you, Peter, but I cannot marry you. Not now. Not ever."

He looked at me with that childish, begging expression. "Oh, Celeste, please marry me. I will give you anything in the world you want."

"Peter, it wouldn't matter what you gave me. I don't love you and I can't marry you."

He was stricken. "I can't live without you, Celeste," he said and the tears rushed to his eyes.

"I'm sorry, Peter, but it wouldn't work," I said.

When we landed at the airport in New York the next afternoon Peter said, "You will at least continue to see me, Celeste."

"No, Peter," I said. "Please don't call me. I am not going to see you again."

That night back in my apartment I was very depressed. I remembered that night in the emergency room over a year ago, the night I had made money my god. Now I'd had the chance to have all the money in the world and I'd thrown that chance away. Money wasn't my god anymore.

Well, if money wasn't my god, what was? I wondered. For the first time in my life I thought of committing suicide.

Chapter XI

The Pimp

Early one afternoon the intercom rang. I picked it up.

"My name is Ming Lee," the girl said. "J. D. Cromarity said you'd see me."

J. D. was a john from the Jet Set. "Come on up," I said.

When the doorbell rang I looked through the peephole. A beautiful Chinese girl was standing there.

"I'm Ming Lee," she said as I opened the door.

She walked in. Tears welled in her eyes and she could not speak.

"What's the matter?" I asked, leading her over to the couch.

"Oh, Celeste, could I work for you?" she asked.

When I hesitated she said, "Oh, please take me in. I've been living with this pimp and I can't stay with him any longer. We just had a fight and I ran out."

The tears started rolling down her cheeks. "He is never satisfied with the money I bring in. He wants more girls. And he likes to go to bed with two girls at the same time. I can't take it because I love him."

Now she was crying uncontrollably, her thin shoulders shaking.

"What's his name?" I asked.

"Raul Fernandez," she said.

"Raul!" I said. "I know him. I met him a couple of years ago."

When I was living with Frank I'd met Raul at a Spanish restaurant where he worked as a waiter. He was the most striking man I'd ever seen—six feet four inches tall and powerfully built. He had black hair, a square jaw, and clear green eyes that burned right through you. His smile was startling, gleaming white teeth against a dark complexion. But even when Raul smiled, his eyes were menacing. When we left the restaurant that night, Frank told me about him.

"A guy sold a kilo of heroin to Raul that was cut with milk sugar. When Raul discovered it, he went after the guy and split his belly open and left him on the street to die. He was a suspect, but the police couldn't prove Raul did it. Another time one of his prostitutes began to slide. She was bringing in less and less money. One night Raul went into a rage and burned her breasts with a cigarette lighter."

I looked at Ming. She was still sobbing.

"You can stay with me, honey. Don't worry about Raul. I won't let him hurt you."

A couple of days later Ming and I were alone in the apartment when the doorbell rang. I wasn't expecting any johns or girls. Besides, they knew enough to call on the intercom first. I went to the door and looked through the peephole. I recognized Marsha, a prostitute who had worked for me months ago. She was so heavy into heroin I had asked her to leave.

"What is it, Marsha?" I asked.

"I'm in trouble, Celeste," she said. "Could I come in and talk to you?"

I looked through the peephole again to be sure no one else was there; then I opened the door slightly. In that instant Raul jumped in front of her and as I tried desperately to slam the door, he pushed it all the way open. He'd been standing against the wall out of view.

"Get out of here!" I screamed.

With one punch he knocked me to the floor. Then he dragged me by the hair across the living room and kicked me in the back.

I couldn't move from the pain and as I watched, he cut the telephone cords from the wall. Ming was screaming in a corner of the hallway. Raul grabbed her and beat her head against the wall until she slid unconscious to the floor. He threw the coffee table against the wall, breaking the legs off. Next he kicked the television set over, breaking the glass. Then he went into my bedroom and called out to Marsha, "Seven hundred bucks, baby!" He'd taken the cash from my bag that I was going to put in the safe deposit box that afternoon. I could hear him dumping the dresser drawers upside down, cursing and flinging them against the walls. I knew what he was after. He wanted my ledgers on the johns. I got up from the floor, ran across the living room and opened the door to the terrace. If I attracted enough attention, Raul and Marsha would have to leave. I climbed over the terrace and was hanging by my fingers from the railing, screaming as loud as I could. The ground was sixteen stories below but I wasn't worried about falling. I was worried Raul would find the books. I kept screaming and now the doorman was directly below looking up at me with horrified eyes. Immediately he disappeared and I saw a few people running into the garden. One woman stood next to the center fountain and cried out, "Oh, my God, she's going to jump!" I went on screaming and then I heard sirens. In another minute four cops were standing below. A fire engine roared down the street and in the next few seconds a ladder was put up against the wall of the building and a net was spread.

Two policemen were now standing on the terrace a few

feet from my fingers and I realized Raul and Marsha had left.

"Miss, if you'll just calm down we can help you," one of the policemen said gently.

I stopped screaming.

"Miss, just hang on and we'll pull you up. You're going to be all right. Stay calm. Don't move." The cop's voice was soothing.

He was inching his way toward me and then I felt strong arms lifting me. He carried me back into the apartment and I collapsed on the couch, hysterical. The cops were standing over me and one of them kept saying, "You're all right now. Everything is going to be all right."

I stopped crying and noticed two medics lifting Ming onto a stretcher.

"How is she?" I asked.

"She'll probably be okay," one of them said.

I sat up and dried my eyes.

"Tell us what happened," one of the cops said, "but first we need some information on you."

I gave them my name and said, "I'm a belly dancer. My girl friend Ming asked me to take her in because she wanted to leave her boyfriend, Raul. That's the guy who was in here. I took Ming in a couple of days ago and Raul was mad at her because she had left him. And he was mad at me for taking her in."

I was careful not to let on that Raul was a pimp because they would wonder what the connection was. I gave them Raul's address at the restaurant where he worked.

One of the cops brought me a glass of water. "Miss Clemente, you should go to the emergency room for treatment," he said.

Before I could get off the couch, a photographer and reporter walked in. I decided to play it cool and I gave them the same story I'd given the police.

Later I was treated at the hospital for bruises on my back. Then I spoke to a doctor about Ming.

"She has a fractured skull, but she's going to be all right. She'll have to rest and take it easy for at least six months," he said.

Later that day I went to visit Ming. She had regained consciousness. "The cops were here to talk to me," she said. "I have to press charges against Raul."

"Don't worry about it," I said. "How do you feel?"

"My head feels like it's going to explode. The doctor says I have to take it easy for several months. My brother and his wife came to visit me and I'm going to be living with them until I'm better."

"That's good," I said.

I stayed only a few minutes because Ming was in such pain.

"Don't give Raul another thought," I said. "When it comes time to go to court, you'll be too sick."

"Okay," she said.

That night when I went to bed I took two Seconols. When I got into prostitution I never realized there would be so much danger, so much agony. I can't go on much longer, I thought. Then, as always, I began to fantasize. Some night I would meet Prince Charming. We would fall in love and he would understand and forgive me for what I'd been doing. And he would take me out of this madness and we would live happily ever after.

Early the following afternoon when Lana, Melanie and I were having our breakfast coffee, the doorbell rang. I looked through the peephole and saw a small, tough looking man I did not recognize. From his appearance I knew it meant trouble. "What do you want?" I asked.

"Raul wants you to know that he's going to rat you out if you don't drop the charges," the man said and left.

The next day I was called into the district attorney's office. I had to go through the story all over again for a cop in the Robbery Squad.

"That will be all, Miss Clemente," he said.

"I want to drop the charges," I said.

"You can't do that!" he said. "Miss Clemente, you've got to press charges against this man. We've been trying to get this guy for years for other crimes, but we haven't been able to do it. Now since he robbed and assaulted you and destroyed all that property, it's a big break for us. By pressing charges you will be helping to put a dangerous criminal in prison."

"I realize that," I said quietly, "but I still prefer to drop the charges."

"If you don't want to think of yourself, you've got to think of other people," the cop said. "You should press charges. This is a very serious matter."

I couldn't let on to the D. A.'s office about Raul's threat, so I had to go along with them. "You're right," I said. "I'll press charges."

The following week I went to court. Raul's attorney approached me in the hallway. "Miss Clemente," he said, "Raul has told me about your business. The best thing for you to do for yourself and for my client is to cooperate with me."

"How do I do that?" I asked.

"The judge will ask who hit whom first. When he does, be sure to say you hit Raul first. This is important, crucial for your own good as well as his."

An hour later as I stood before the judge and he questioned me, I said, "As soon as Raul Fernandez entered my apartment, I slapped him across the face."

Within minutes the judge dismissed the case.

During the next two weeks I was called back to the district attorney's office a few times for further questioning about Raul. No matter how many questions they asked and no matter how they tried to trip me up, I never let it slip that Raul was a pimp. If they ever made the connection, I was doomed.

The last time I was called in, I was questioned by Detective Donahue, head of the Robbery Squad. Detective Donahue was a good-looking man in his thirties with dark hair and brown eyes. He had a strong jaw and firm mouth and was the most masculine-looking guy I'd seen in a long time.

"Miss Clemente, I realize you've been through a great deal," he said kindly. "I don't want to needlessly upset you but we have to find out all we can about Fernandez."

For such a young man he was very serious.

"I've told the other detectives all I know," I said.

"It would be for your own protection if you could tell us anything more," he said, looking at me steadily with genuine concern.

"I really don't know anything else about him," I said.

I wondered if he knew Raul had murdered that drug dealer a couple of years ago.

"You realize that when the case was dismissed, you were put in jeopardy," he said.

"I'm not worried," I said. "I don't think he'll bother me again."

"If your friend Ming Lee comes back to your apartment, he very well might," he said.

"Ming is staying with her brother in New Jersey until she's well," I said.

"Why do you think she didn't show up in court for Fernandez' trial? She was supposed to testify against him."

"She's in love with him," I said.

"But when the police were in your apartment, you told them Ming came to you because she wanted to leave Fernandez," he said.

· "Oh, that was just a lover's quarrel," I said.

He asked me a few more questions and once again he went over all the facts of that day two weeks ago when Raul had wreaked such havoc in my apartment. This detective had an unhurried way about him, but I was aware that unlike the other detectives, he was careful and precise to an extreme. And under his pleasant, considerate, easy manner I sensed a rapid-fire intellect.

"That's enough questions," he said and smiled. With that smile he was another person, charming and appealing.

I felt butterflies in my stomach.

"Would you care to join me for lunch, Celeste? he asked.

"I'd love to," I said.

This was completely unexpected.

Over cocktails Ray said, "I'm glad Fernandez didn't do any permanent harm to you, Celeste."

"God's on my side," I said and laughed.

Ray looked at me thoughtfully. "You shouldn't dismiss Fernandez so easily. He is a very dangerous man."

I was touched by his concern and I was amazed that he hadn't made any personal remarks. Ray Donahue wasn't like any man I'd ever met.

"I'll be all right," I said.

"I hope so," he said. "I can't understand how a man can strike a woman. I see it all the time in my work, but I'll never get used to it."

I wondered what he'd think if he knew of the years I'd lived with Frank, taking all those beatings, and the years my mother and I had been beaten by my father. There was something so good and decent about Ray. "You're a very gentle person, aren't you?" I said.

"Just an average guy, that's all," he said and smiled. Once again with that smile he was transformed.

Then he looked at me in a new way. Something was happening between us and I couldn't hold his glance any longer. I was glad when the waiter handed me a menu.

"I recommend the baked clams," Ray said.

As we ate, other detectives from the D. A.'s office came into the restaurant. Several stopped at our table to talk a few minutes. It was obvious they all liked and respected Ray Donahue very much.

I was sorry when we had finished our lunch. I could have talked to Ray for hours.

"Would you go out with me some evening soon?" Ray asked.

"That would be nice," I said and hoped the excitement didn't come through my voice.

The following day, unknown to me, the district attorney's office secured a court order to put a tap on my telephones.

Chapter XII

Prince Charming

When Marta, one of my new girls, came in one afternoon she had a beautiful white Persian cat in her arms. "Where did you ever find such a beautiful cat?" I asked.

Marta rubbed her cheek against the cat's head. "Isn't she gorgeous? A friend of mine sold her to me because part of her tail was cut off in an accident. My roommate doesn't like cats so I thought maybe you would like to buy her. She's only $50 and she has papers."

I took the cat from Marta and held her against me. "What's her name?"

"Suki," she said.

Suki cuddled against me and put her head on my shoulder. "I love her," I said. "I'll give you the fifty dollars."

"I'm glad Suki's found a home," Marta said.

I put Suki down and she walked slowly, majestically across the living room with that tail standing straight up. "She knows she's gorgeous!" I said.

All of us were laughing.

"She used to be a show cat," Marta said.

"I'll have to buy a beautiful collar for her," I said, "and a bed."

"And food," Melanie said. "I'll fix her dinner every day."

Saturday afternoon Melanie and I went to Manhattan and I bought a rhinestone collar for Suki and a white mink pillow for a bed. "I'll bet there isn't another cat in the world with a mink bed!" Melanie laughed.

"Only the best for Suki!" I said.

When we were back in our neighborhood we stopped at a grocery store and bought jars of baby food, eggs, catsup and cream.

"I happen to know that a cat with class likes scrambled eggs with catsup," Melanie said.

With the sparkling collar against her white fur and that regal walk, Suki became everybody's favorite. Each afternoon Lana brushed Suki. And Melanie made a soft scrambled egg with catsup for her. Later in the day Melanie mixed baby food together for Suki's main meal. And whenever she wanted it, Suki had a saucer of cream.

Monday afternoon Roland Barbaro was the first one to call.

"Celeste, do you have anybody new?" he asked.

"Yeah, Roland. I have a Norwegian girl, Marta. She is a beauty, 39-23-36."

"I'll be over in an hour," he said.

Later when Roland was leaving the apartment he said, "Call me as soon as you have a new girl."

I laughed. Roland wouldn't go with the same girl twice.

He came over two or three times a week and was soon a fixture in the apartment. One time he called and said, "Celeste, I'd like to bring over an assemblyman tomorrow afternoon."

"Fine," I said. "Who is he?"

"The Honorable Ed Cumari," he said.

"Oh, wow!"

When I told the girls who was coming over the next day they became very excited. When Ed Cumari came in I was surprised. I hadn't expected a man who would come to a house of prostitution to be so formal. He was a nice looking man in his early fifties and impeccably groomed. Roland introduced us and I said, "Hi. How are you?"

"I'm pleased to meet you, Celeste," he said. "I'm very well, thank you. How are you?"

I took him into the living room to look over the girls and it was obvious he liked Lana. He gave me $100 and they went into Lana's bedroom.

Roland took Anita, a new girl, into a bedroom.

I was talking on the phone when Melanie came over to me.

"Where's Suki?" she asked. "She always wants her dinner at this time but she's not here."

I cut the telephone conversation short, but before I could start looking for Suki there was a loud cry from Lana's bedroom. Two seconds later Lana came out, holding her stomach and laughing hysterically. Suki came bounding out after her.

"Suki jumped on the assemblyman's head right in the middle of everything!" Lana said, falling into a chair.

Two minutes later the Honorable Ed Cumari emerged from the bedroom fully dressed. Without looking at anyone and without saying a word, he crossed through the living room and went out the door.

I received a call one afternoon from Jeb Richenbach, a philanthropist known throughout the country. We talked for a few minutes and he said, "Celeste, I'd like to come over and meet you."

"I'm sorry," I said, "but I don't know you personally."

"But I'm Jeb Richenbach!" He was incredulous.

"I'm Martha Washington," I said and hung up.

A week later Rob Davenport, a Wall Street tycoon, brought Jeb Richenbach over. Jeb and I sat in the dining room away from the others. "When you turned me down last week," he said, "that's when I knew I had to meet you."

I smiled. "In this business you can't be too careful."

He laughed. Then he said, "Celeste, if I may say so, I

cannot understand how you could be in this business."

He glanced over at the girls in the living room. "Your girls are beautiful," he said.

"Which one would you like?" I asked.

I was sure he'd choose Melanie because she looked as though she traveled with the jet set.

"I won't have anyone but you," he said.

"I'm sorry, that's not my department," I said. "I'm the madam."

"Then I'd like the tall, dark-haired girl," he said.

I called Tracy over and he paid me and they went into a bedroom. After Jeb left the apartment, Tracy came over to me. "That guy is a real weirdo," she said. "He refused to take his clothes off. He said if he got undressed, there wouldn't be any excitement in it."

"You meet all kinds in this business," I said, laughing.

The following week Detective Ray Donahue called. "Celeste, I've been fighting this," he said.

"Fighting what?" I knew.

"You," he said simply. "Would you have dinner with me Wednesday night?"

"Where can I meet you, Ray?" I asked. I wasn't going to let him find out what I was doing.

He gave me the name and address of a good French restaurant on the west side of New York City.

"See you at 10 p.m. Wednesday," I said and hung up.

I couldn't wait to see Ray. I hadn't felt like this about a man since I'd known Frank.

Wednesday night I wore a red sheath dress. When I walked into the restaurant Ray was standing at the bar, watching for me. He had on a dark suit and white shirt with striped tie. I hadn't realized just how good looking he was. He walked over to me and took my hand. "You look terrific!" he said.

When he looked into my eyes I knew the same thing was happening to him that was happening to me.

We sat at a table near the piano and Ray ordered Manhattans.

"How have you been since I saw you?" he asked.

"No problems," I said.

"If Fernandez ever comes around again, give me a call," Ray said. He took out a pen and slip of paper and wrote a number down. "In fact, if you need any kind of help don't hesitate to call me, Celeste."

My own brother couldn't have been more concerned about me. "Thanks Ray," I said. "I'll remember that." I asked him about his work.

"I like it, but there are times I don't get any sleep. There's no such thing as an eight-hour shift. When they need me I have to be there."

He took himself very seriously and he seemed a little tense.

"I never went out with a cop before," I said.

"I hope it won't be the last time," he said and smiled.

Later Ray looked at me earnestly. "Celeste, I don't have a line like most guys."

"I'm glad," I said. "When you say something Ray, I know you mean it."

"That's for sure," he said.

For the first time in months I began to relax. Ray was such a decent person. And in his quiet way, he was more attractive than any man I knew. He was so gentle, so considerate I had to keep reminding myself he was a cop.

After dinner we walked around the city, enjoying the summer night. I was surprised and pleased that at no point did Ray take my hand. He was basically very shy.

"It's getting late," I said.

"Do you have time for a drink?" he asked.

"Just one," I said.

We went to a lounge and after we sat down at a table Ray reached for my hand. In that gesture I knew that something had been settled between us.

When I finished my drink I said, "Ray, if you don't mind I have to leave."

"Will I see you again?" he asked.

"How about Monday night?"

"I'll meet you at the same place at ten o'clock," he said.

I left immediately before either of us could say anything further. The attraction between us was powerful and I didn't want to spoil anything by rushing.

The next afternoon the girls and I were sitting in the living room talking. Hilda, a girl from Germany, had just started working for me. She was a statuesque blonde with smoky grey eyes and she couldn't speak a word of English.

"Roland will love her," I said.

"Yeah," Lana said. "With him you don't have to say a word. In fact he prefers no conversation."

The phone rang and I answered it.

"Celeste, this is Randy. How are you?"

"Great," I said. Randy worked in City Hall.

"I have a very special guy I'd like to bring over. Do you have a gorgeous blonde?"

"I have two gorgeous blondes," I said. "Who's so special?"

"Larry Hamilton," he said.

"What?"

Larry Hamilton was a major league baseball player, an idol of millions.

"You're kidding!" I said.

"I'm not kidding!" he said. "Wait 'till you see him!"

"Well, bring him over!" I said.

When I told the girls who was coming over there were shrieks of delight. They were crazy to meet this ball player. A half hour later when Larry Hamilton walked in with Randy there was dead silence. After standing in the living room with Randy for a couple of seconds, Larry broke the ice by introducing himself to the girls.

"We never would have known," Lana laughed.

He took to her right away.

After that we started getting calls from other baseball players. Then nationally known football players began coming over. The more prestigious the johns, the more money I charged. We were making more money than I'd ever hoped for.

More foreign girls began working for me. Many of these girls could speak very little English, but this only enhanced their attractiveness for the johns. I had to be careful how I arranged appointments. I didn't want johns to meet each other in my apartment.

I'd been meeting Ray twice a week and I was uncomfortable with the arrangement. I was really falling for him and I hated to be around any other man. I was beginning to feel like a hypocrite, although I had nothing to do with any of the johns myself. Now when Ray and I were out together he had me absolutely spellbound. I never thought I could feel like that again after the years with Frank. I wanted to have an honest relationship with Ray, but then I'd have to level with him. I cared too much for him and he was too decent for me to go on living this lie.

The next time he called he said, "Celeste, would you like to have dinner in a very special place where there's good food and wine and hardly any people?"

"Sounds fabulous," I said.

"Tomorrow night at ten?" he asked.

"Fine," I said.

He gave me the name and address of a Lebanese restaurant on the East Side. I wondered if he was ready to tell me how he really felt. I knew he felt the same way I did. I also knew he was a man who did not take love lightly.

The following night I met him in the Lebanese restaurant. Candles flickered at each table and a string quartet played softly. Ray ordered whiskey sours and then he looked at me and said, "You're so beautiful, I don't know why you bother with me."

"Bother with you!" I repeated. I wanted to say, "I love

you!" Instead, I looked down at my cocktail and I knew I could not continue with the act any longer. There was nothing in the world I wanted more than Ray's love and that could never be.

He took my hand. "What's the matter, Celeste?"

"Nothing," I said, looking away.

I felt the pressure of his hand and looked back at him. "Everything's wrong, if you want to know the truth," I said.

"Tell me about it," he said gently. "Maybe I can help."

Tears stung my eyes. "I can't tell you here," I said.

He called the waiter and paid for our drinks and we left. "We can have dinner later," he said. "Now you're going to tell me what's bothering you."

I walked in silence by his side. He put his arm around my waist and drew me closer. I wished with all my heart that I could erase the past. Ray was so honest, so conscientious that when I told him the truth he would either turn me in or would drop me and I'd never see him again. Tears were coursing down my cheeks. Ray stopped and pulled me against him. "I won't let you cry," he said, kissing me on the forehead. He took out his handkerchief and handed it to me.

I couldn't speak and the tears just kept coming. We continued walking; then Ray guided me firmly into a building. I looked up. It was a hotel. I didn't care. I had made up my mind to tell him the truth. If I lost him and the business too, I didn't care. I was so in love with him that if I couldn't have him for my own, I didn't want to live.

In the next minute we were in an elevator, then walking down a hallway. Ray unlocked a door and we were in the privacy of a room. He took me in his arms.

I stopped crying and whispered, "Oh, Ray!"

"I know how you feel, Celeste," His voice was husky. "I feel the same way. Ever since that first time when we had lunch together."

I drew back a little to look at him. "Ray..."

"Shh!" He put his finger on my lips.

"Ray, there's something I..."

"Later," he said and he covered my mouth with his.

For the first time in my life I knew what it was to love and be loved in return, completely and without reservation.

Ray took my face in his hands. "I love you, Celeste," he said.

"Oh, Ray," I said, "I love you with all of my heart!"

"This isn't going to be any ordinary love affair," he said. "It has been building up so powerfully, it had to happen like this."

"I know," I said and then I began to cry uncontrollably.

"Hey, what's the matter?" he asked.

"I've been living a lie," I said. "For the past year and a half I've been a madam, running the biggest prostitution ring in New York."

He pulled me against him. "I don't care what you've been doing," he said in that husky tone. "I love you and that's all that matters."

Later that night in the apartment when I went to bed, for the first time in my life I was completely happy. I was in love with a wonderful man who loved me inspite of what I was. It was almost too good to be true.

Business began to snowball and now I had thirty girls rotating. I had two black girls, a mulatto girl, a Japanese girl, two Chinese girls, girls from Italy, Norway, Germany, Sweden and France, besides all the white American girls. I'd learned long ago that the key to success in this business was variety.

I saw Ray every Wednesday and Friday night and I always met him at a restaurant or a lounge. One time when we were together I said, "Ray, would it hurt you if you called for me at my apartment?"

"I love you and I trust you so it wouldn't have the effect on me that you think it would," he said.

"I'm glad you trust me, Ray," I said. "I have never been

unfaithful to you since I've known you and I never will be."

"I believe you, Celeste," he said. "And I'll be honest with you. I don't like what's going on in your apartment, but I don't have the right to object. Just so you're exclusively mine, that's all I ask."

"You know I am," I said. I wondered if the day might come when he would feel he had the right to ask me to give up prostitution.

I seldom had johns in the apartment at night and the following Wednesday, only the girls were there when Ray came over to pick me up. He spent a few minutes talking to Melanie and Lana and I could see they liked him immediately. They were happy for me and it was no secret I was in love.

The next day when the girls and I were having our first cup of coffee Lana said, "Ray is really a nice guy. And let's face it, what could be better than having a friend in the police department!"

"He's the nicest guy I ever met," Melanie said. "Mr. Nice Guy!"

We laughed and the name stuck. After that my girls always referred to Ray as Mr. Nice Guy.

Roland Barbaro brought over another assemblyman and during the next week we started getting calls from other politicians in Albany. The girls and I looked forward to meeting men who had made it to the top, whether it was in sports, business, or politics. But we were learning that the more money they had, the more screwed up they were and the bigger degenerates they were.

One time a group of politicians from Albany was giving a party in a suite of hotel rooms. A couple of other madams and I were invited and asked to bring along some of our girls. Tracy and Marta went to the party with me and when we arrived the men were very drunk. Call girls were going in and out of the bedrooms every ten minutes. When Tracy came out of a bedroom she said to me, "This guy had his shoes under the bed and in one shoe I could see a wad of bills. As I left, I reached down and took $500!" She laughed. "That's besides the $200 he paid me!"

When she repeated the story to Jeanette, a girl from another house, Jeanette said, "That's nothing. I just took the guy for $1,000!"

As time passed, I got more and more johns and along with the increase in business, the pressures mounted. There was the constant fear of the police busting in. I had to be a detective myself, always watching the girls, anticipating every threat and possible danger. And now there was the conflict of being so deeply in love with Ray and continuing with this life.

One night when I was out with Ray I said, "Sometimes it's too much, worrying about girls overdosing, worrying about someone ratting me out. I wouldn't be the first madam to be turned in."

"You've been reading too many detective stories," he said. "But seriously, Celeste, if you're ever arrested call me. If I'm not there leave a message and say 'I'm jammed up.' That way I'll know you've been arrested and I'll come right over." He took out a cigarette and tamped it on the table. "I've got my problems too," he said.

"What kind of problems?" I asked.

"I should have told you long ago," he said. "I'm sorry now that I didn't."

"It can't be that bad," I said.

"I'm married, Celeste, and I have three children."

"Oh, is that all?" I was relieved. "Ray, as long as you love me, that's all that matters," I said.

He put his hand over mine. "I do love you and I always will."

"I appreciate your honesty," I said, "but it won't affect our relationship."

It did though. When I went to bed that night I couldn't fall asleep. I realized now that for the past month I had been hoping to marry Ray some day. He was not only the man I loved, he was the man who was going to take me out of this way of life. Ray was my Prince Charming.

Chapter XIII

International

By this time most of our johns were celebrities of one kind or another. Many were listed in the Social Register and the politicians now included congressmen from Washington. We started getting johns from other countries, men who either had top positions in government or traveled with the jet set. There was one thing that all of them had in common and that was their attitude. Not one of them was interested in becoming involved with a girl. It was just hit and run from one to another. And the more money they had, the more prestigious they were, the greater the demand for orgies. I had more and more homosexual boys over and the longer these orgies went on, the weirder they got. It was clear to me that the johns were interested only in smoking pot, snorting coke, getting high and having an orgy. I made up my mind if they wanted a freak scene, I'd give them a freak scene they'd never forget. There was no fighting this thing. You either got into it or got out of it, and I got into it.

The girls and I had become so accustomed to famous johns and subsequent disillusionment, that we no longer got excited when a john with a big name was coming over. One afternoon a congressman we knew called to ask if he could bring over an ambassador. When I repeated the name to Lana, she hit her hand on the arm of the chair and said, "If the people of this country ever knew these men were coming here, they would die!"

When the congressman and ambassador walked in, I took them into the living room and introduced them to the girls. The congressman walked over to Lana and began talking to her.

"You get my vote!" she said.

He laughed and they went into Lana's bedroom.

The ambassador, a man from the Far East, turned to me and said, "Celeste, I like you the best."

"Sorry," I said. "My job is to stay out here and answer the phones and the door."

"Then I'd like Hilda," he said.

After the men left I took Lana aside. "You shouldn't talk like that to a congressman," I said.

"He went with me, didn't he?" she asked. "Besides, Celeste, that's the way I am. It's part of my charm," she said and winked.

A couple of weeks later a congressman brought in a nationally known criminal attorney, Cornelius Seligman. He was a wiry man with excessive energy and quick, darting eyes. As he sat at the dining room table talking to me, he kept drumming his fingers on the table. "Do you ever relax?" I asked.

"Relax?" He looked at me strangely. "That's a word I don't understand. I work hard, harder than anyone I know. I can't slow down and relax. If I did, I'd explode." He glanced over at my girls.

"Which one would you like?" I asked.

"I'd like that beautiful, petite one with the sweet expression."

I called Melanie over. He paid me and they went into her bedroom.

An hour later when Cornelius Seligman left, Melanie said to me, "That guy is a nut. He handed me his belt and told me to beat him first."

The longer I was in this business, the more sick johns I met. It was always a relief to go home on a Sunday and forget about my real life. A few days later I was sitting with Mother in the kitchen, talking about Chris and my sisters. She brought me up-to-date on their activities and the longer she talked, the sadder I felt. I wanted to have the kind of life they had. I wanted a husband and a house of my own and two or three children. I wasn't there long when Grandma came into the house.

I got up and hugged her, but I could see right away she had something on her mind. She kissed me and we sat down again in the kitchen. Grandma didn't waste a minute with small talk. "Celeste, I'm glad you came out today. The Lord has put a burden on my heart for you," she said. "Ever since you were seven years old the Lord has had a calling on your life and I will never, never, never give up until you come back to Him."

I could not be around Grandma when she talked like this. "I have to go now," I said.

As I walked into the living room and put on my coat, Grandma called out, "Celeste, you must obey God!"

I ran out of the house, got in my car and headed back to my apartment. I never should have gone out to see mother so early in the day. My Sunday visit had been a waste of time. Now I was so angry and frustrated I was more impatient than ever to see Ray. When I was with him I could forget about everything.

Ray had called for me at the apartment just that one time. I was more comfortable meeting him on the outside.

Wednesday night I met him at a lounge in mid-town. As soon as we took a table, he began questioning me. "Celeste, how did you ever get into prostitution?" he asked.

"I got into prostitution because I needed the money to get into show business," I said. "Otherwise, I would have been starving like all the other young actresses."

"Celeste, with your looks and intelligence you could have been a success in anything," he said.

"Anything except what I wanted to do," I said.

"It's a shame you ever got mixed up in this," he said.

"Ray, believe me, I never planned to get into pros."

He regarded me with that thoughtful, grave expression so characteristic of him. My being a madam was getting to him and I wondered if his love for me was strong enough now that he might ask me to get out of this business.

Later in a hotel room I put my arms around him and said, "You know that ever since we went to bed that first night last August, I've been faithful to you."

He pulled me against him. "I believe you, Celeste."

"Ray, you're the only real man I've ever known," I said, "the only man in the world I can trust."

He looked down and didn't say anything. Compliments embarrassed him and this was just one more reason I loved him so.

Business was building up at an incredible pace. Calls were coming in from Rome, Madrid, London, Paris, Tokyo, Hong Kong, Mexico City, Caracas and countless other cities. As the worries and pressures mounted I had to be on my toes every minute. I could never relax, not for a night, not for a minute. I had to be sure none of my girls was carrying drugs. And on my daily trips to the bank, I was forever looking over my shoulder for a junkie, a pimp, a cop, or someone from the Mob who might want to rob me or rub me out. The only way to cope with all these pressures was to drink more and more heavily. But now even drinking in the afternoon couldn't ward off my increasing depression.

I started taking bennies when I got up but then when I went to bed I couldn't sleep. So now I was taking a seconol every night. We had a supply of thousands of uppers and downers from Dr. Bolan. As the weeks went by this pattern began to spiral into more depression, heavier drinking and more pill popping. Little by little something was happening to my mind. I wondered how much longer I could go on smiling for the johns, how much longer I could be a pillar of strength for my girls.

One Thursday night when I met my girls in the after hours club in the Village, they greeted me with shrieks of delight. "We've been waiting for you!" Lana said. "Brent Durant has invited all of us to a party at his hotel!"

"Brent Durant!" I cried. He was one of the biggest Hollywood stars of all time.

When we arrived at Durant's suite of rooms, a man met us at the door. "All you girls can't come in here," he said. "There's not enough room."

"Brent Durant invited us," I said. "I'm in charge. Just ask him to come to the door."

The man looked the girls over and said, "I screen who comes in here. You and the little one can come in," he said, pointing to Melanie.

Tracy groaned. "I'll wait out here," she said. "Maybe the rest of us can get in later."

Melanie and I made our way through a throng of people toward Brent Durant, who was standing in the center of the living room. He towered over everyone and was even more handsome in person than on the screen. As we approached him, he caught sight of Melanie. He broke into a smile and motioned her over. Immediately people parted to allow us to walk through.

Reaching for Melanie's hand, he said, "You're the most beautiful girl here."

Melanie introduced me and Brent said, "Celeste, I think you'll agree that if Melanie could act, she'd be a star overnight. I've never seen such beauty!"

I smiled and Brent put his arm around Melanie's waist.

"It will cost you $300," I said.

"Melanie likes me," he said, pulling her closer to him.

"Put up or shut up," I said.

"I don't have to pay," he said. "There are plenty of girls who will go to bed with me for nothing."

"Then you're with the wrong girls," I said.

"Oh, I'm not so sure about that," he said, glancing at Melanie.

"Come on, Melanie," I said. "We don't need this."

Melanie let go of his hand and Brent Durant leaned down and said, "Melanie, when you get rid of Celeste, come back."

When we were out in the hallway I said, "There are guys just as big as Durant who are willing to pay."

One of them was Dwain Dunbar, a nationally known vocalist. Dwain came into the apartment on a Thursday night for an orgy. As soon as he walked in, the girls were mesmerized by him. He smiled at me. "Celeste, your place is first class," he said, looking around the living room. "There isn't any good house in New York that I haven't been to, but this beats them all."

Later in the evening when he was leaving he was an entirely different person, downcast and depressed. "What's the matter?" I asked.

"Would you meet me for dinner later when you're through here?" he asked.

I hesitated and he said, "I just want to talk. Things are getting to me."

"Okay," I said.

He gave me the name of a restaurant and I said, "See you at eleven."

When Dwain and I were seated in the restaurant he said, "Celeste, you're an intelligent young woman. I just have to talk to someone tonight and you're it. Do you mind?"

"I don't mind," I said. "Unload."

"You know, I've had everything I've ever wanted. I've tried every thrill. I've been on every drug, every high. And now that I'm at the pinnacle of my career, I'm scared."

"Scared? What are you afraid of?"

"I'm not even sure what I'm afraid of," he said. "I've learned that it's all for nothing. There are no kicks left. There is no woman who can interest me for more than an hour and most of them bore me in five minutes. I've been married three times. There's no lasting love, no kind of security. There's nothing. What in the hell is it all about, will you tell me?"

I forced a bright smile. "It doesn't matter what it's all about," I said. "Whatever you do best, that's what you've got to keep doing."

None of these guys had any peace. With all their fame and fortune, with all their education and talent, they were more confused and miserable than the underprivileged people I'd known.

I lived for the two nights a week I spent with Ray. By this time he knew the story of my life, starting with my childhood when I would try to help my screaming mother, only to end up being beaten myself. There was no one who knew as much about me as Ray and no one who cared as much.

Friday night I met him in a Swedish restaurant uptown. I had on a white crepe dress and my hair was hanging in waves to my shoulders, the way he liked it. When he took my coat he said, "Why do you do that to me?"

"Do what?" I laughed.

"Dress like that," he said.

When we were seated he said, "Celeste, sometimes I wonder why you go out with me. You could have any man you want."

"Ray, you're the only man I want. You know that by this time."

"And you're the only girl I want," he said. "When we

first met I never thought this would happen."

His eyes had that troubled look and I wondered how long it would be before he would tell me that he couldn't go on like this, being married to someone else and being in love with me. I'd known Ray almost four months now and I knew he could not continue leading a double life, just as I knew he could not live without my love.

"I feel like I've known you all my life," I said.

"That's good," he said. "All my life I was half dead and didn't even know it until we fell in love."

"Another thing, Ray," I said, "I met you just in time."

"What do you mean?"

"Well, if I hadn't met you when I did, I think I would have cracked up by now. I have so many problems with my girls, so many fears about drugs and cops. I can't trust anyone and I think I'm being followed."

"Celeste, you worry too much." He smiled reassuringly. "You're getting paranoid on the subject."

"Maybe," I said, "But Ray, I'm sure my phones are tapped."

He laughed. "Come on, honey. You've been watching too many police stories on TV."

He had a way of making everything seem all right.

Later in a hotel room Ray was more ardent than at any time before. "I love you, Celeste," he whispered. "I never knew it was possible to love a woman like this."

He looked at me with such love, such pain that I cried out, "Oh, Ray, how much longer can we go on like this?"

"I don't know," he said. "I just don't know."

Before I fell asleep that night I thought about Ray. He was too decent a guy to rush into a divorce and I would never pressure him. I knew now that it was only a matter of time when he would tell me he was getting a divorce and we could be married. Every moment away from him was agony. He needed me as much as I needed him. He had reached the point where he would give up his wife and children and I would gladly give up all the money I was making to marry him.

The next afternoon when I was talking to Melanie about Ray she looked concerned. "Celeste, you wouldn't leave everything and run off with Ray, would you?" she asked.

"Melanie, you don't have to worry. No matter what I do, I'll always take care of you."

She smiled. "I couldn't make it without you," she said.

That afternoon it was business as usual. The first call was from Roland Barbaro. This time he was in a rush and instead of asking if I had anyone new, he said, "Celeste, I'll be over in an hour."

"Fine," I said.

I didn't have anyone new for him but four of my best girls were there. When Roland walked in he looked around the living room quickly. Then he came over to me and in a lowered tone, said, "May I speak to you privately?"

I walked into the kitchen and Roland followed me. Nellie the black maid who cleaned on Thursdays, was busy washing out the cabinets.

"You made me come over here for nothing!" He spit out the words. "You know I will never go with the same girl twice!"

"If you recall, Roland," I said evenly, "you didn't ask if I had someone new."

"Well, you should have known," he said. "You should have told me not to come over!"

Then I saw him staring at Nellie.

"I'll take her," he said.

"What?" I couldn't believe it. "You can't take her. She is working for a cleaning agency."

I couldn't imagine why he would want to go to bed with an ugly, old black cleaning woman who looked as though she would break in two if you touched her.

"Please!" he said. "Ask her."

I went over to Nellie and in a barely audible voice extended the invitation for him. Her eyes widened in amazement. Then quickly regaining her composure, she said, "All right, I'll do it."

Nellie and Roland went into a bedroom and I poured myself a double straight Scotch and thought, "Some day I am going to get out of this business. Some day I am going to leave all this behind forever!"

Chapter XIV

The Holidays

On Christmas Eve Melanie and I decided to dye Suki green for the holidays. I mixed vegetable coloring with water and Melanie held Suki in the sink as I dyed her beautiful white fur.

"She'll be the only green cat in the world!" Melanie laughed.

"Tomorrow we'll take her to my family's. They'll go crazy when they see her," I said.

Suki put up a fuss but eventually every hair of her white ermine coat was a bright Christmas green. When we were finished Suki ran around the apartment, shaking herself, trying to get rid of the moisture clinging to her fur. "Melanie, get your hair dryer quick," I said.

She came back with the dryer and in five minutes Suki was comfortable.

Christmas morning I was awakened by the loud jingling of the telephone. I looked at the clock. It was eleven o'clock. Who in the world would be calling this place on Christmas I wondered, and in the morning yet. I picked up the receiver.

"Merry Christmas, Celeste!" a man's voice said. "This is Fred Bently. Could I come over in about an hour?"

"Just who the hell do you think you are, calling me on Christmas day! Don't you have any respect?"

"Respect? Respect for what?" he asked. "Hey, remember you're running a house of prostitution, not a church."

"I don't care," I said. "It's still Christmas."

"The day of the year doesn't change the truth," he said. "Come on, Celeste. I'll give you $200."

He was right. Whether I let him come over or not wouldn't change the fact that I was running a house of prostitution. Besides, he was too good a customer to lose.

"Oh, all right," I said. "Come over at one o'clock."

At twelve o'clock when Melanie got up I said, "I don't like to ask you to do this on Christmas, but Fred Bently is coming over."

"I don't care," she said. "Christmas is just another day in the year as far as I'm concerned."

Having a john in the apartment on this sacred day made me furious. After he left, I was so depressed I didn't want to see anyone. We gathered our gifts together and with Suki we went downstairs and got in my Cadillac. As we drove over the parkways I couldn't force myself to talk.

"Celeste, don't let it bother you," Melanie said.

"I can't help it," I snapped. "The whole day is ruined."

"But I'm the one who went to bed with him," she said.

"It doesn't matter. I'm the madam. I'm the one who agreed to have him over. Oh, God, sometimes I wish I were dead!"

When we reached my home I forced myself to smile when Mother opened the door. Melanie had Suki and Mother took the cat from her and laughed. "I never thought I'd live to see a green cat!" she said.

We walked in and put our presents on the floor under the tree. Dad was in his arm chair, stoned as always, the bottle on the end table with a half-filled glass. I could smell the turkey roasting in the oven and when we went into the kitchen to talk to Mother, I began to forget. Suki investigated every corner of the kitchen and helped restore my spirits. Later the three of us had dinner while Dad slept in his chair. At the end of the meal Mother put a pot of tea on the table.

"This is the first Christmas I've enjoyed since I was a little kid," Melanie said and her lower lip started quivering.

Mother pulled Melanie against her. "You're one of the family now, Melanie," she said. "We love you."

With those words the tears started coursing down Melanie's cheeks. Mother put both arms around her and began rocking her like a baby. Hard as I tried I could not keep back the tears.

In a couple of minutes Melanie stopped crying, drying her face with a napkin and apologizing.

Mother kissed her and stood up. "How about some apple pie?" she asked. Things were under control again.

"Just so it's homemade," I said.

"Baby, you know I wouldn't have any store-bought pie in the house." She laughed.

"When can I give out my presents?" Melanie asked.

"Tonight when Chris and the girls come over," Mother said.

"Do I have to wait that long?" Melanie cried.

We laughed. She was such a kid.

"Oh, Melanie, get your presents and give them out now," I said. Christmas was worth it just to see the joy it gave Melanie.

She went into the living room and came back with two boxes.

I watched while Mother opened a large box. It was a long red robe. "Melanie, it's beautiful!" she said. "I've always wanted a warm robe."

Melanie's face sparkled as she watched Mother put it on.

Then I opened the small box Melanie gave me. There was a gleaming gold clip for my hair. "Melanie, you shouldn't have!" I said.

She was bubbling over with happiness now. I got my gifts and handed Melanie a long, slim box. She opened it and smiled. "Oh, Celeste, I've never had cultured pearls! They're beautiful!"

I handed Mother a gold envelope. She opened it and took out two five-hundred dollar bills. "Oh, Celeste!" I thought she was going to cry.

"I told you I'd make it big in show business," I said.

In the evening my sisters dropped by with their families and I gave each of my sisters $50. After they'd gone home Chris came over with his family and I gave him $50. He kissed me. "You're too good to us," he said.

"Not good enough is more like it," I said. Chris held a special place in my heart. During all those terrible years when I was a child, Chris more than anyone had protected me from my father.

Later he went across the street to get Grandma.

"She's not feeling very well lately," Mother said.

When Grandma came in I was shocked. Her beautiful eyes had lost their glow and she looked completely worn out.

I ran to her. "Grandma!" I cried. I put my arms around her and buried my face in her neck. In that moment I realized how much Grandma meant to me and I couldn't bear the thought that one day she would be gone. I fought back the tears and reached for her gift. Grandma opened the box. It was a white shawl with a hundred-dollar bill pinned to it.

"God bless you, child!" she said. "You always had a big heart!" Then her face took on the joyful look I knew so well. "Celeste," she said, "Jesus has told me that I will live to see you come back to Him!"

I said nothing. Melanie gave me the eye and I broke

away from Grandma and started toward the kitchen.

"I'm going to make some coffee," I said.

That night before falling asleep I prayed. "Oh, God, please forgive me for what I'm doing. Don't let me die and go to hell. When I'm eighty years old I'll serve you, I promise!"

The following day we went back to the apartment. "I have to get away from this place," I said to Melanie. "I can't stand the holidays. I wish I could black out for the next week!"

"Why don't you visit your friend, Jane?" she suggested.

"That's a good idea," I said.

Jane was the only friend I had who was straight. She worked as a buyer in a department store and had an apartment in Manhattan. I seldom saw her but we kept in touch by phone. I'd known Jane since I was in high school. She knew what I was doing and when I'd seen her a couple of months ago I'd told her about Ray. She was always after me to get out of prostitution.

I called her early that evening. "Could I come over tonight, Jane? Things are pretty bad," I said.

"Of course you can. You know that, Celeste."

At seven o'clock I was in her apartment.

"Hi!" she said. "You look like you could use a drink."

She mixed a Scotch and soda for me.

"It's getting to be too much," I said. "I've got johns from all over the world, and nothing but the best—socialites, politicians, stars of stage and screen, and the biggest names in sports."

"God, that's some operation!" she said.

"Will you believe these johns are worse than the ones I used to have? The higher up these guys are, the more screwed up their heads are. They're the most miserable bunch of degenerates I've ever met!"

"Celeste, when are you going to get out of it? You're only going to end up getting hurt or killed," she said.

Jane knew about the dangers, about my arrest last year, about Ida being murdered.

"I'm holding on until Ray asks me to marry him," I said.

"What if he doesn't ask you? Have you thought about that?"

"He'll ask me," I said. "I know he will. It's only a matter of time."

"I don't think it's worth it, Celeste. I think you should get out while you can. Right now."

"Just a little longer," I said. "Then I'll go straight."

I stayed a couple of more hours and by the time I left I felt better.

The following afternoon Tony called. "Celeste, how about a little holiday night clubbing?"

"I could use it," I said.

We went to the club owned by Tony's nephew in Little Italy. Everyone there was in the Mafia. Tony led me to a large table in the center. He sat down at the head of the table and I sat on his right. To my right was a couple I had never seen before, Carmine Delgardo and Audrey Shaw. I'd heard of Carmine. I couldn't remember the particulars, but his name was in the news regularly. I knew he was high in the Mob. Audrey was a striking platinum blonde with dark brown eyes. When Carmine got into a discussion with some of the men at the table, she said in a lowered voice, "I can't stand this guy. I've got to get away from him."

I laughed. "You shouldn't have a problem finding someone else," I said.

"That's not the point," she said. "I can't talk here."

I gave her my telephone number. "Call me tomorrow," I said, "and we'll talk."

I liked Audrey. She was completely natural and direct, something like Lana but she lacked Lana's whacky sense of humor.

The next day Audrey called and we talked for a long

time. "I'm so glad I met you," she said. "I feel I can trust you."

"I've never broken a confidence," I said.

"Carmine, the guy I was with last night is supporting me," she said. "I've been his mistress for almost a year. Carmine is a big man in the Mafia. Very big. The problem is. . ." Audrey began crying. "The problem is that I'm in love with someone else. I met Jerry Fortunato a couple of months ago and I'm living with him. Carmine found out about Jerry and twice he's tried to have him killed."

"Oh, God!" I cried.

"I'd do anything to get away from Carmine," she said. "If I didn't need the money, I'd dump him."

"What about Jerry? What does he do?"

"Jerry could never support me," she said. "He's a sweet, handsome guy but he's a truck driver."

"Audrey, I have the solution for you," I said.

"What solution could there be?"

"You can work for me," I said. "I'm a madam."

"You're kidding!"

"I'm serious. Look, you don't have to depend on Carmine anymore."

"I don't think I could do it," she said.

"Audrey, with your looks and my connections, you could make it big!"

"I don't know," she said. "I just don't know."

"You work in pros for a couple of years, then quit and buy a legitimate business. It would be an investment for you."

"I don't think I could do it," she said.

"Well, if you change your mind," I said, "call me."

I had no way of knowing that the police suspected Carmine Delgardo of killing another Mafia figure, Joe Rizzo and his girl friend, Anna Marino, just as I had no way of knowing that my phone had been tapped since last August. These two murders had been under investigation for over five years and although the D.A.'s office couldn't prove Carmine had committed them, they had reason to believe he had. As a result of this telephone conversation with Audrey, the D.A.'s office thought I was indirectly connected with the Mafia and a massive investigation was begun on me.

The next night I met Ray at our favorite French restaurant. He ordered a bottle of champagne. "This is a special occasion," he said. "Our first Christmas season together."

I smiled but I wanted to cry. I wished that I'd had the right to have Ray with me all Christmas day.

He took out a very small gift-wrapped box from his pocket and put it on the table in front of me. My heart nearly stopped. The box was so small, I thought it might be a ring. I opened it quickly. It was a gold chain with the initial "C" hanging from it. "It's lovely," I said. I hoped the disappointment didn't come through my voice.

I handed Ray his gift. It was a lighter. When he opened the box, he smiled. "Thanks, Celeste. I really needed a lighter."

"Are you going to make any New Year's resolutions?" he asked.

I laughed. "I know myself too well," I said. "How about you?"

"For the past few years I've made the same resolution," he said. "I'd like to get out of police work and become a lawyer."

"A lawyer!"

"I've always wanted to be a lawyer," he said. "I think I'd be good at it."

"You're good at police work," I said.

"Yes, but I don't like it as much as I thought I would. I'd rather defend people than investigate them."

"Well, it's not too late, Ray. Maybe you should go to law school."

Ray was too nice a guy, too sensitive for police work. He would be happier as a lawyer and he certainly had the mind for it.

"Some day, maybe," he said.

Later when we were in a hotel room, Ray said, "When we met, Celeste, I didn't intend for this to happen."

"Are you sorry?" I asked.

"Are you kidding? I'm just sorry we didn't meet years ago." He kissed me for a long moment. "I love you, Celeste," he whispered.

"You're the only man I've ever loved, Ray," I said. "I thought I was in love with Frank all those years, but now I know you can only love once."

"Only once," he said. "I've never loved any woman the way I love you."

That was the closest he'd come to telling me he didn't love his wife. I knew he didn't love her but he was too honorable and decent to say anything against her. Now I knew for certain it wouldn't be long before Ray would get a divorce.

Two days before New Year's Eve I received a letter from Fernando Lopez. He had enclosed round trip plane tickets. The letter read, "Dear Celeste, The tickets are for you and Melanie. Come down for New Year's Eve weekend. I've made reservations at the usual place."

"Melanie!" I cried. "Pack your things, honey. We're going to Puerto Rico!"

"When?"

"We have reservations for tomorrow from Fernando."

She laughed. "Wonderful!"

"I can't think of a better time to get away from this scene!" I said.

Late the following afternoon we were in San Juan. In our hotel room I telephoned Fernando.

"I'm so glad you could come down!" he said. "Enrico and I will be over at six o'clock to take you girls out for the night."

Melanie and I enjoyed our dinner with the men but when we walked into the casino later, my heart dropped. I nudged Melanie. "Look who's here," I said.

She followed my eyes. "Oh, no!" she said.

Two of our johns from New York were standing at the Black Jack table. As we walked in they saw us and smiled. Fernando, who never missed a thing, said, "You have friends vacationing down here?"

"It's a small world," I said.

Fernando gave me $400. "See what you can win tonight," he said.

I took the money and started playing roulette. By the end of the evening I had doubled my money and then quickly lost all but $50. It was 3 a.m. when Fernando came over to me and put his arm around me. "Ready to go back to the hotel?" he asked.

He could hardly stand. I was disgusted with him.

I turned to Enrico. "I'm not getting in the car with him," I said.

"Don't worry," Enrico said. "I'll drive."

When we were outside Enrico pushed Fernando into the back seat and Melanie and I got in the front. Before we got to the hotel Fernando had passed out.

When we were inside the hotel I said to Melanie, "That's the last time I'm seeing Fernando. I can't stand his sloppy drinking."

We went into the lounge for a nightcap and as soon as we sat down the two johns walked in. "Oh, God, I don't believe it," I said. "It looks like they're following us."

Melanie looked up. It was too late to walk out. Jack Sherman and Chet Ranior were walking over to our table. "Perfect timing," Chet said. "Can't think of any two girls we'd rather have."

"We came here to get away from you people!" I said.

"Come on, Celeste!" Jack said.

"Sorry," I said, "we're on vacation."

They left and we went to our room.

"We should have stayed in New York," I said. "Fernando is the sloppiest alcoholic I know and meeting those two johns was the last straw!"

"Maybe we'll have a good time tomorrow night," Melanie said. "Enrico said the club we're going to has the best band on the Island."

The following night we were dressed in our best formals. Melanie wore a pale blue chiffon gown with a row of cultured pearls I'd given her. Her dark hair was drawn back from her face, setting off her high cheekbones and making her grey eyes seem even larger. I wore a fucia silk gown and my diamond necklace. My hair was swept up. As we waited for the men I called room service and ordered a bottle of champagne. A few minutes later Melanie and I had our first toast.

"In four hours it will be the new year!" Melanie said, holding out her glass.

I touched her glass with mine. "Here's to getting out of our business!" I said.

We were laughing and joking but by nine-thirty when the men hadn't arrived, we weren't laughing anymore. At ten o'clock the phone rang. I answered it and by Fernando's slurred speech I knew he wasn't going to make it over. "Celeste, please forgive me," he said.

"Forgive you!" I was furious.

"I won't be able to make it tonight," he said.

"That's obvious!" I said and slammed down the receiver.

Melanie and I went down to the lounge of the hotel and got stoned. Everyone in the place had a date and most of them were married couples. I'd come to Puerto Rico to fight off a depression and everything had been going wrong. A feeling of desperation began to overwhelm me.

New Year's day when we got up, I opened the glass doors to our balcony and looked out. I saw men and women sitting in lounge chairs and a few people swimming. A young couple was walking around the pool. The woman had an infant in her arms and the man held a little girl's hand.

"Daddy, pick me up!" the child cried.

The man picked her up and he and his wife exchanged a smile.

Tears stung my eyes. That's what I wanted—a family. More than anything in the world I wanted Ray as my husband. I wanted my own little baby. I wanted to put a bottle in his mouth. I wanted him to dribble all over. I wanted to hear him say, "Mommie!"

I turned away and closed the doors. "Melanie," I said, "you and I are young and beautiful. We have money and can buy anything and go anywhere, but we have nothing. Absolutely nothing!"

"You know what, Celeste? It doesn't bother me," she said. "I just don't care."

"Let's go home right now," I said.

"What's wrong with you? For the past two months you haven't been acting right!"

"It's because I'm so close to getting what I've wanted all my life and I don't think I can wait any longer."

"You mean Ray?"

"I mean Ray."

Two hours later Melanie and I were at the airport, going home a day ahead of time. When we took our seats on the plane we saw Jack and Chet across the aisle. We nodded. "Let's not get involved in a conversation with them," I said. We picked up the magazines in front of us and began reading.

A few minutes later we fastened our seat belts and the plane roared down the runway. I hated takeoffs. I held my breath as the plane picked up speed. Finally it lifted and was airborne. About fifteen minutes later the plane started bouncing around. Then suddenly it plummeted.

In the next instant it lifted sharply upward. Then immediately it began to fall again. I felt as though my stomach was in the top of my head.

"Ladies and gentlemen, there is nothing to worry about," the pilot's voice came through the intercom. "We are experiencing some weather. Please fasten your seat belts. We should be out of this in a few minutes."

We had already fastened our seat belts. Suddenly the plane plummeted. "My God!" I screamed. "We're going to be killed!"

Melanie reached for the white bag and was sick to her stomach. I heard women crying all around me. The plane shot upward.

"Ladies and gentlemen," the pilot said again. "We are returning to San Juan as a precautionary measure. There is no cause for alarm."

A stewardess was coming down the aisle, smiling reassuringly at the passengers. "There is no cause for alarm," she said.

I began to pray. "Oh, God," I said, "please don't let anything happen. In my condition I'd go straight to hell. If I get out of this plane alive, I promise You that I will get out of prostitution!"

After what seemed like an eternity the plane landed. As it taxied down the runway I called out to the stewardess. She came over to me. "I want my money back," I said. "I'm not taking this plane back to New York."

"Miss, there is no need to change flights. We are going to wait until the weather changes, then go to New York."

The plane had come to a stop. I jumped from my seat. "I will not stay on this plane another minute!" I screamed. "I demand my money back. I'm taking another plane to New York!"

I made such a scene she was glad to get me off the plane. "Go to the ticket office," she said. "They will book another flight for you."

Three hours later Melanie and I were airborne in another plane. When we were back in our apartment late that night, I turned on the radio. During a news broadcast we learned that the plane I had refused to take back to New York had crashed, killing sixty-three passengers. Jack and Chet were among the dead.

Chapter XV

"There's Room at the Cross for You"

Larry, the steerer from Associated Press, called. "Celeste, I have a new girl for you. Lucy is a beautiful strawberry blonde. She had a small part in an off Broadway musical last year."

"What's her problem, Larry?"

"No problem," he said. "She's a dancer out of work."

"Okay, send her over. I just hope she's not another junkie."

Before Lucy arrived Roland Barbaro called.

"Celeste, do you have anyone new for me?" he asked.

"In less than an hour, Roland, I'll have a beautiful strawberry blonde. She had a big part in a Broadway musical last year."

"I'll be over at 3:30," he said.

I had to have my hair done but now I couldn't leave. I called the beauty salon downstairs and asked them to send up an operator. Minutes later Kurt, a young boy, came in. He shampooed my hair in the kitchen sink and wrapped a towel around my head. Then we went into the dining room and he began to set my hair.

A few minutes later Lucy arrived. She was a pretty girl, taller than my other girls. She had beautiful legs.

"Hi!" I said. "Tell me about the musical you were in."

Lucy sat down at the table and began relating one story after the other about her experiences in show business.

Kurt was still setting my hair when Roland arrived. I introduced Roland to Lucy and I could see him eyeing her legs, but as we talked Roland began looking at Kurt. When Lucy asked Roland a question, he answered without looking at her. He couldn't take his eyes off Kurt. I could see what was happening.

"Celeste, I'd like to speak to you alone," Roland said.

I got up and went into the kitchen and Roland followed me.

"I want the boy," he said. "Ask him if he'll go with me."

I returned to the dining room and in a lowered voice I spoke to Kurt. "Roland wants to know if you'll go with him."

Kurt's eyes brightened. "Yeah, sure," he said. "I've turned tricks before."

Being around degenerates was not something I could get used to. Just the opposite in fact. The longer I was in this business the more revolted I was by these people. The longer I was in this business, the more depressed I became.

When I met Ray on a Friday night in the middle of January, I was on the verge of losing all control. We went to the Lebanese restaurant we liked so well and as soon as we were seated I could see something was troubling Ray.

"What's the matter?" I asked. "Are you worried about something?"

"Me, worried?" He smiled. "You know better than that."

"Maybe you're just tired," I said.

"Not too tired," he said. His glance traveled over my face and rested on my mouth.

"I love you," I whispered.

"Hold it until later," he said.

Ray was a very private person. He never showed affection in public. Maybe that was why he was so demonstrative when we were alone.

I studied him and suddenly I was tired of holding my feelings in. I couldn't go on any longer with this make believe world of dressing up and eating out, snatching love now and then in a hotel room. I wanted a real life. I wanted to wake up with Ray in the morning. I wanted to cook his breakfast and have his dinner ready when he came home. I wanted him all to myself for the rest of my life.

"What's the matter with you tonight, Celeste?" he asked.

"I'll tell you later," I said.

As soon as we were in the hotel room I burst into tears. Ray put his arms around me and held me against him. I was sobbing now.

"Hey, what brought all this on?" he asked.

I broke away from him. "I love you too much to go on like this any longer," I said. If I hadn't been so depressed I never would have said such a thing.

"I know what you mean," Ray said. "Do you think it's easy for me?"

Before I could say another word, he was kissing me. "I love you, Celeste," he said. "Always remember I love you."

In all the months I'd known Ray, he'd never been so intense, so emotional. "Oh, Ray, I never knew what love was until you," I said. "I love you with all of my heart."

"Always remember I love you," he said.

Later in the apartment when I was alone I thought it was probably the best thing that could have happened, crying and telling Ray I couldn't go on any longer this way. It was better to be honest and open. It had brought out a depth of tenderness and love in him that I'd never known before. And over and over again he'd whispered almost urgently, "I love you. Always remember I love you."

A couple of days later when Lana, Melanie and I were having our breakfast coffee, Tracy called from the intercom downstairs.

"Come on up," I said.

When she walked into the apartment she was crying. Tracy never cried.

"What happened?" I was alarmed.

"It's Evelyn," she said. "She's dead."

"Oh, no!" I cried.

Lana jumped to her feet. "An overdose?"

"No, it wasn't an overdose," Tracy said. "It was murder."

"Oh, my God!" Melanie cried. "How?"

"Evelyn had one big fault that finally did her in," Tracy said. "She was a rat. She'd been busted for prostitution many times in the past couple of years. She used to brag to me that she always got off because she turned someone in."

"Who did she turn in?" I asked.

"Raul Fernandez," Tracy said. "He was released from prison a few days ago and he befriended Evelyn. She never suspected that Raul knew she was the one who turned him in three months ago. Anyhow, yesterday he told her he had some really good stuff and she bought it from him. Last night she shot up with rat poison."

I poured myself a double Scotch. What next, I wondered. All the stories I'd heard about Raul came back to me and I could never forget what he'd done to me last summer. Jane was right. I should get out of this business before I got hurt or killed. For the next few days I couldn't shake the sense of doom hanging over me.

One night I awoke suddenly with my heart pounding. I didn't know what was wrong until I remembered that Ray had not called me in four days. He always called on Tuesday to make a date for Wednesday, but Tuesday he hadn't called. And all day Wednesday he didn't call. Maybe something had happened to him. When he hadn't called by Friday afternoon I was almost out of my head with worry.

"What's the matter with you, Celeste?" Lana asked.

"Ray hasn't called," I said. "I haven't seen him or heard from him in a week."

"He must have a good reason," she said.

"He's never gone more than four days without seeing me or calling me," I said.

"Maybe he's sick," Lana said.

"I think I'll call his office," I said.

In all the time I'd known Ray, I'd never called him. When the sergeant answered the phone I said, "Is Detective Donahue there?"

"Detective Donahue isn't in today," he said. "May I take a message?"

"Yes. Please tell him Celeste called," I said and hung up.

Ray did not return my call that day or over the weekend. When he didn't call Monday I became so depressed I couldn't talk to the girls. As the days passed I began to feel that this wasn't really happening to me. When I hadn't heard from Ray in two weeks I called his office again.

"Detective Donahue isn't in today," the sergeant said. "May I take a message?"

"Yes. Tell him Celeste called and I'd like him to call me back," I said.

"All right, Miss. I'll leave the message for him."

That day I received calls from several of our most prestigious johns. They wanted an orgy Friday night. I contacted my best girls and asked several homosexual boys over. At ten o'clock Friday night the place was packed. When the last john came in I said, "I won't be able to stay. An emergency has come up and I have to leave town."

I put on my mink coat and got in my car and drove into Manhattan. Maybe Jane would be home. When I reached her place she was out. I couldn't face the freak scene going on in my apartment so I checked into a hotel. After I'd had six Scotches I took a Seconol and went to bed. I still couldn't sleep. All I could think of was Ray. What had happened to him? Why hadn't he called me in over two weeks? He loved me with every fiber of his being. And he was so thoughtful, so kind, it wasn't like him to let me suffer like this. Maybe he had decided he didn't have the heart or the money to leave his wife and kids for me. Still he would have told me. It was out of character for Ray to just drop out of my life. I went over every word and incident of the last time we'd been together. He'd never been so loving, so ardent. "I love you, Celeste. Always remember I love you," he'd said over and over again. Now those words took on an ominous connotation. *Always remember I love you.* Had Ray known that night that he would never see me again?

A few days later, hoping to shake the deepening depression, I called Tony and asked if he and Victor would come over.

"Celeste, I'd love to come over with Victor," he said. "I have my brother, Augie, visiting me. Could you get a girl for him?"

"Sure," I said.

"We'll be over tomorrow night at seven," he said.

I was fond of Tony and he didn't make any demands of me. If I just wanted to have dinner and play cards, it was all right with him.

The following night the three men came over and Lana, Marta and I served a special Italian dinner. Later when we were in the living room drinking, instead of getting high, I was becoming more morose. The others were laughing and having a good time. Marta came over to me. "Follow me," she said.

I went into the kitchen with her. "Celeste, you have got to unwind," she said. The next thing I knew she was holding a spoon up to my nose. "Here, sniff this," she said.

I sniffed the stuff and went back to the living room. Victor and Lana were dancing and Marta and Augie went into one of the bedrooms. I sat on the couch not paying attention to what Tony was saying when suddenly my heart started beating rapidly. Then it began beating so fast and hard, I was afraid I was going to have a heart attack. I stood up and began pacing back and forth. I could hear Marta and Augie talking right behind me, yet I knew they were in the bedroom. "I'm going to kill her!" Augie said in a loud voice.

"It will be so easy," Marta said. "And no one will ever know."

They were running after me. I dashed across the living room and opened the door to the terrace. I stepped outside and looked down. The ground seemed very close, only a few feet away. Yet I knew we were on the sixteenth floor. I put one leg over the railing and heard Lana scream. Then I felt strong arms around me, dragging me back into the living room. After that I didn't remember anything.

The next day Tony called. "Celeste, you came within an inch of losing your life last night!" he said. "It took all my strength to pull you back on the terrace. You shouldn't sniff coke. You had too much!"

I only vaguely remembered running out on the terrace. Now I was frightened. Maybe I had crossed that line. Maybe my mind was going to snap. Maybe it had already snapped. Ever since that plane crash on New Year's day, I'd been jinxed. It had been one thing after the other. It seemed that nothing was ever going to go right again.

Three weeks had passed and Ray hadn't called. I was desperate. I called his office and again the sergeant said, "Detective Donahue isn't in today. Would you like to leave a message?"

Recalling Ray's words of almost six months ago—"If you're ever arrested, call and say 'I'm jammed up,' and I'll come right over,"—I said, "Yes, tell Detective Donahue that Celeste called. Tell him I'm jammed up."

"I'll leave the message for him, Miss."

When a few more days passed and I still hadn't heard from Ray I knew something was drastically wrong. Now I was angry. If Ray had decided he couldn't leave his wife, I

could understand it. What I could not understand and
what I could never forgive was that he hadn't told me.
Without a word, without a hint, he had dropped out of my
life.

It was almost four weeks since I'd seen Ray when I went
to Jane's apartment for dinner. "Celeste, what's wrong? I've
never seen you like this," she said.

"I can't go on," I said. "I think my mind is going to snap."

"What about Ray? I thought you were holding on until
he got a divorce."

"I haven't seen or heard from Ray in a month," I said.

She handed me a drink. "Celeste, you have got to forget
about him. You have to get out of pros before it's too late."

"I know," I said.

"Knowing isn't enough," she said. "Every time I see you,
you're in worse shape than the time before. Get out of that
life and get out now!"

"You're right," I said. "I should get out."

"Don't wait any longer," Jane said. "Your girls are only
going to get you into trouble. If one of them is in another
house and gets busted, she's apt to turn you in or give your
code to the police. A girl could say something about you
to the wrong guy and you could end up having your brains
blown out."

"What can I do instead?"

"You can do a lot of other things," Jane said. "You could
get a job in my store as a salesgirl and in a year's time with
your brains and looks, you'd be a buyer. You can go right
to the top!"

"Jane, could I stay overnight in your apartment?" I asked.

"Of course you can," she said.

I didn't bother to call my girls. I didn't want to listen to
their complaints about not getting their money tonight. I'd
give it to them in the morning.

The next day I got up with Jane and drove her to work.
Then I headed out of Manhattan to go back to my place.

While I was driving through the crowded city, I turned on the radio. By mistake I had turned to a gospel station. A man's voice filled the car with the strains of an old familiar hymn. "There's room at the cross for you. There's room at the cross for you. Though millions have come, there's still room for one. There's room at the cross for you."

Tears were sliding down my cheeks as my mind flashed back to the little Pentecostal church where I used to sing that hymn.

"Oh, God!" I cried out. "Get me out of this business. I can't take it anymore!"

Chapter XVI

The Raid

Melanie, Lana and I were having coffee when the phone rang. I picked up the receiver and said, "Hello."

I could not believe my ears. It was Ray. My heart started thudding.

"I've been out of town," he said. "I know I should have called sooner. I'm sorry, Celeste."

I wouldn't let on that I was falling apart at the sound of his voice. "How have you been?" I asked calmly.

"Fine," he said. "Listen, Celeste, a buddy of mine just came in from Dayton. He's here for a few days to see the World's Fair. Could you fix him up with one of the girls?"

I was stunned. After all this time he wasn't asking to see me! And he had the nerve to ask me to fix up a friend of his. I wanted to scream. "Sure, Ray," I said. "I'll be glad to." I was on guard. Something was wrong.

"Andy likes blondes," Ray said.

"I'll get Lana," I said. "Call me back in an hour."

I hung up. "Of all the gall!" I screamed. "I don't hear from him for a month and the first thing he wants is for me to fix up a friend of his!"

I ran to my bedroom and threw myself on the bed, sobbing. He hadn't asked me out. He hadn't even asked how I was. There hadn't been a trace of the old love in his voice, the love he'd never been able to keep out of his voice. In rage I beat my fists into the pillow. Finally I got control of myself and went back to the girls.

With icy calm I said, "Lana, I want you to take care of a friend of Ray's."

"Sure," she said, "but I can't turn any tricks today, Celeste. This is my day to visit my baby and mother."

When Ray called back I said, "Lana is visiting her family today. How about tomorrow night at nine?"

"Tomorrow at nine," he said and hung up.

That was all. I was shocked, but after four weeks of silence, after telephone calls not returned and the "jammed up" message ignored, I shouldn't have been shocked at anything.

That night I drank more Scotch than ever before and when I went to bed I took two Seconols.

When the girls and I got up the next day Lana said, "I feel like my head is going to blow off!"

"You probably had too much to drink last night," Melanie said. "Have some coffee."

Lana began sipping the coffee and then she ran to the bathroom and was sick to her stomach. When she came out she said, "Oh, God, I'd rather break a leg than throw up."

"Lana, go back to bed and you'll be all right in an hour or so," I said.

She went to her room and closed the door. Two hours later when she hadn't come out I went in to look at her. I put my hand on her forehead. She was running a temperature. What would I tell Ray? Yesterday Lana was visiting her family. And now today she was sick. He'd never believe me. I called a couple of johns and broke Lana's appointments. Then I called Ray. "Gee, I'm sorry but Lana can't see your friend today," I said.

"What!" He was annoyed.

"She's sick," I said. "She's got a bug. Why don't you call me tomorrow at two o'clock. Maybe she'll be better by then."

"Andy will be disappointed," Ray said slowly, "but I guess I can hold him off for another day."

I was seething. I couldn't believe that he was talking like this. For the past six months we had lived for each other. Now it was as though he hardly knew me.

Lana was sick to her stomach again that afternoon and then she had chills. "I hope this is just the twenty-four hour grippe," I said to her.

"I don't care what it is," she said. "Celeste, I have to get a fix. I'm going to Manhattan. I don't have any stuff here."

"Okay," I said. I knew she'd be out of her head in a few more hours without a fix.

The following day when we got up Lana was a little better. Her stomach had calmed down.

"I'm weak," she said, "but I'll be okay in a day or so."

She went down to the garage and shot up and then went back to bed.

At two o'clock Ray called. "Can I bring Andy over to-night?" he asked.

"Ray, I'm sorry but Lana is still sick. Could you put Andy off until tomorrow?"

"Come on, Celeste!" he said. "This is the third time I've called!"

I wanted to say something to hurt him, but I restrained myself. "I wish I had another blond for your friend," I said, "but I don't have one available today."

"How about Melanie?" he asked.

Something was up but I pretended not to suspect a thing. "She's booked solid," I said.

"Well, maybe Lana will be feeling better by tonight. Let's make it at eight o'clock," he said.

There could not be the slightest doubt now that something was wrong. "Maybe you're right," I said. "Come over tonight at eight."

"Good. See you at eight," he said and hung up. I'll fix

him, I thought.

Lana got up at six o'clock. "I could eat some soup and crackers," she said.

"That's a good sign," I said.

Tracy and Melanie came in and I ordered three steak dinners and the soup and crackers from the restaurant downstairs. Then I told them, "You have to be at the Park Sheraton at nine o'clock to meet a couple of tricks, but first I want you to have your hair done."

After dinner when they got up to leave, Melanie leaned over impulsively and kissed me on the cheek. "See you in a little while," she said.

It was after seven when they went downstairs to the hairdresser.

"Am I going to turn a trick with Ray's buddy tonight?" Lana asked.

"Not tonight," I said casually. If there was going to be a problem, I didn't want Lana involved. Besides, I had a plan. "You go back to bed and stay there," I said.

"It's all right with me," she said. "I'm really not up to it anyhow."

I showered and put on a pair of slacks and a sweater. At eight o'clock the doorbell rang. I looked through the peephole. It was Ray and his friend. I opened the door and they came in. Ray glanced at me and quickly looked away. Andy was an attractive guy in his mid-thirties with sandy hair and deep blue eyes. We went into the living room and sat down on the couch. "This is a nice place you have," Andy said.

Ray wasn't looking at me.

"Thank you," I said. I kept a smile on my face while the anguish and anger of the past weeks boiled into a fury.

Ray, looking around the room, said, "Where's Lana?"

"She's sleeping," I said.

"Can't you wake her?" he asked.

I stood up and with one of my brightest smiles I said, "I'll take care of Andy myself."

"What!" Ray was shocked. "Let him go with Lana!"

"Lana isn't feeling well," I said, still smiling. I glanced at Andy and it was clear that he was disturbed about something.

"But I never would have..." Ray didn't finish whatever he was going to say.

"Come on, Andy," I said as I started toward my bedroom.

Ray was fuming. Andy followed me into the bedroom and I closed the door. "How much will it be?" he asked, handing me $100.

"It's on the house," I said. "You're a friend of Ray's."

"Celeste, I hate to do this," he said, "but I have to put you under arrest." He pulled out his badge.

"What!" I was incredulous. Then my knees buckled and I screamed, "Oh, no! My God! My God!"

I ran into the living room. Ray was on the phone. "Send the boys up," he said. He was talking to the Vice Squad.

"I'm going to kill myself!" I screamed at him. "And I hope you have it on your conscience for the rest of your life!"

He wouldn't look at me. His face was a dark red.

"How could you do this to me?" I screamed. "And to think I really believed you loved me! Oh, my God!"

I began pounding my fists on the wall and sobbing hysterically. Andy came over and took me by the arm. He guided me to a large arm chair. "Sit down, Celeste," he said. "Get hold of yourself."

As I fell into the chair sobbing, Lana ran into the living room. "What's going on?" she cried.

Andy went over to her. "I have to put you under arrest," he said. "Sit down on this chair."

"Oh, my God, a bust!" she cried.

"Ray did this," I said to Lana.

"Oh, God!" she cried. "I don't believe it!"

Ray was making another telephone call. I got out of my chair.

"For six months you told me how much you loved me!" I shrieked. "And all the time you were setting me up for the D. A.!"

I collapsed in the chair, sobbing. My mind was so crowded with thoughts and fears I couldn't absorb all that was happening. A minute later the doorbell rang and Ray opened the door. An army of plainclothes detectives came in and swarmed over the apartment, spreading out into every room. There were over thirty of them. Ray was speaking to the lieutenant in a lowered tone.

"Judas!" I screamed.

Ray's face was drawn into tight, hard lines and a muscle in his right cheek was twitching. He spoke briefly to the lieutenant and left, never once looking at me.

Two cops were standing next to my chair and two more were standing next to Lana's. A policewoman came over to me. "All right," she said. "You and your girl friend get in the bathroom. I have to examine you."

Lana and I walked into the bathroom. We had to strip and the policewoman examined our persons. "Put your clothes back on," she said, "and get back in your chairs and stay there!"

We took our seats and the same cops were there to guard us. The policewoman began walking around the living room, studying the oil paintings. There was a buzz of activity throughout the apartment as cops were talking and laughing softly. About ten of them had gone into my bedroom. From where I was sitting I could see two of them trying on wigs. Then they danced around the room. Another cop came up to the one in the blond wig. "Oh, honey, you're cute!" he said. "What's your name? How much will it cost me?"

Other cops were going through my dresser drawers. They emptied my pocketbook and I cried out, "What are you doing, going through my bag?"

A cop standing next to my chair said, "Your cash and

wallet will be held by the police. You'll get them back later."

A cop in the living room turned on the stereo and another cop started dancing in front of me. "Hey, Baby, how much do you charge?" he asked.

I could hear the cops in the three bedrooms turning everything upside down. I knew they were looking for the books. Two of them were searching the front hall closet. It was only a matter of minutes when they would discover the strong box.

A young cop went up to Lana. "Blondie, let's you and I go to bed!" he said.

The intercom rang and the policewoman picked up the receiver. I knew it was the girls coming back from the hairdresser to change clothes for the evening. Over the intercom the policewoman's voice would sound like mine. "Come on up," she said and hung up.

In the next minute the doorbell rang. One of the cops opened the door and said, "We've been waiting for you girls! Come on in and join the party!"

Melanie and Tracy stepped in and stood there frozen.

"Sit over on the couch, girls," the cop said. "You're under arrest."

"Oh, no!" Tracy moaned. She sat down with a resigned look. Tracy had been busted twice before for prostitution.

Melanie's eyes filled with tears. Then looking at me she began to cry.

Suddenly pandemonium broke out. The cops had found the books in my strong box and ran into the living room. Cops from the other rooms piled into the living room. They were shouting and laughing as several of them opened the books. "Look at this!" one of them said. "I don't believe it!" He announced the names on one page and as each name was called out, most of them from Hollywood, there were catcalls and low whistles.

"Listen to this!" another said. He called out names of

politicians in Albany and Washington.

There were roars of laughter.

"Wait till the press gets a hold of this!" another one said.

A young Irish cop said, "Hey, how does this grab you?" And he called out the names of two major league baseball players.

Another cop doubled over laughing. "Boy, look at this name! I'd like to shake him down!" Then he called out names from the Social Register. The apartment resounded with stomping, whooping and whistling.

Finally they finished going through every book. Most of the cops were in the living room. One of them turned up the volume on the stereo and some of them began doing the bumps and grinds and making obscene gestures. Other cops were passing ledgers one to another. Then I saw a cop come out of my bedroom, carrying a stack of photographs. "Sit down fellas," he said, "and watch the picture show."

All of the cops promptly sat on the floor as he held up a large picture of Lana in the nude. The apartment echoed with whistles. He held up one picture after the other. Then with a picture of a stag party in his hand, he came over to me and said, "You girls are really photogenic!" Then he held up my baby pictures. "You just never know how a little girl is going to turn out!" he said.

I glanced at the girls. Tracy was bored. Melanie was pale with fright. The only thing on her mind, I knew, was getting a fix. And Lana, as always, even in this situation, could find something to smile about.

Someone turned the stereo off. "Okay, girls, get your coats," a cop said. "You're going to the D. A.'s office."

Andy handed me my purse, cash and wallet. "You'll be needing this," he said.

"I'd like to take my jewelry with me," I said.

"Okay," Andy said and followed me into the bedroom.

I opened a dresser drawer and took out the satin slip I kept wrapped around my diamonds. I dropped the jewelry into my bag with the wallet and cash and we left.

We went down in the elevator and outside to the un-marked police cars. Each of my girls was put in a separate car with three cops and then we drove to the D. A.'s office.

Andy was sitting next to me in the back of the car. "Celeste, Ray was told that it was either you or his job," he said. "This raid was politically motivated. The D. A. is running for governor. We're going to blow this thing world-wide. If you cooperate with the D. A. you won't have to do any time."

I didn't have to think long about the deal. "Okay, I'll cooperate as long as you don't use my real name," I said. "Use my alias, Carmen Costello."

"Okay," he said.

Once inside the building my girls and I and four cops got into an elevator. When the elevator stopped and the door opened, it was quite dark in the hallway. As my eyes ad-justed to the dim light, I couldn't believe what I saw. There were three television cameras and about a dozen reporters and photographers. I was the first girl out of the elevator and as I bent over, I yelled, "Melanie, duck!"

I could hear the TV cameras being wheeled down the hall behind us. Flashbulbs were popping and reporters were shouting questions. "What was the name of the major league baseball player?" one of them asked.

"Who was the assemblyman?" another asked.

Inside the waiting room of the D. A.'s office we sat down on a bench and I turned my face to the wall. The reporters and photographers were packed into the waiting room now. "Miss Clemente, is it true you were working with the Mob?" a reporter asked.

I jumped up and shrieked, "Miss Clemente! Where did you get that name?"

The reporter was surprised at my reaction. "From the police," he said.

"Oh, my God!" I cried and fell back onto the bench. Now

my family would be disgraced! I was stunned. I held my head in my hands and didn't even hear the rest of the questions. All I could see was my mother's horrified face. Later I felt someone tugging at my arm. "Come on," a cop said, "the detectives will see you now."

I walked into an office where two detectives were sitting. "Sit down, Miss Costello," Sergeant McPherson said.

"Miss Costello!" I cried. "After you people gave my real name out to the press, now you're calling me by my alias?"

"I'm sorry," Sergeant McPherson said. "That was a mistake. We did not intend that your real name be revealed."

I began sobbing. I couldn't believe what was happening to me.

"This will be much easier on you," he said, "if you will cooperate with us."

"After you people ruined my family, you expect me to cooperate?" I screamed.

The other detective, Sergeant Donnelly, spoke gently to me. "Celeste, we are not enjoying this. It is not our intention to hurt you or your family. Now, if you want to help yourself, you will confess."

"I am innocent," I said.

Sgt. McPherson said, "Celeste, let's get this over with. Just give us some big names. If you will give us the names of a couple of politicians, the D. A. will be satisfied."

"You won't get anything out of me," I said.

"We'll see about that," he said.

He switched on a bright light and turned it directly into my eyes. I was blinded and my eyes began to water. "All right, Celeste, who in the Mob was backing you?" he asked.

"Al Capone," I said.

"Don't get smart," he said. "What do you know about Carmine Delgardo?"

"Nothing," I said.

"One of your johns is a top man in the Mafia," Sgt. McPherson said.

"That's news to me," I said. I knew he was referring to Tony.

"Who did you turn your money over to?"

"A bank," I said.

"Look, this isn't some kind of joke," he said. "You are in serious trouble."

I'd never turned a dime over to anyone, but he didn't want to believe that.

"What about Dick Morrison?" he asked. "Before he was sent to the Drug Rehab Center, were your girls getting coke from him?"

"I don't know anything about drug dealers," I said.

"Come on. Most of your girls were into coke and heroine. We know that. And we're going to find out which dealers they bought their junk from!"

"I had better things to do than keep tabs on dealers," I said.

"You damn little hooker!" he shouted.

"Don't be so rough on her," Sgt. Donnelly said. "Celeste, if you will cooperate, it will be so much easier."

It was a game they were playing. One was the bad guy and one was the good guy. It was standard police practice to get someone to talk.

"Look, we had your phone bugged for six months," Sgt. McPherson said. "We know all about you and your activities so you might as well cooperate."

Six months. I'd known Ray for six months. Ever since that assault by Raul Fernandez. That's when Ray had started asking me out. I closed my eyes for a moment, trying to blot out the blinding light but it was no use. I could still see the white glare.

"Where did Melanie Morrison and Lana Waring get their junk?"

"I don't know," I said.

"What do you know about Raul Fernandez?" Sgt. McPherson asked.

"Nothing," I said. I wondered if they suspected him of

Evelyn's murder.

"Come on, Celeste. When he broke into your apartment six months ago, he told us you were a madam," Sgt. McPherson said. "You must know something about him, something we'd like to know."

So Raul had started this whole thing. And after I had cooperated with his lawyer so he wouldn't rat me out! "I don't know anything about Fernandez," I said.

Sgt. Donnelly took over. "Look, Celeste, we can keep you up all night if we have to. Personally, I do not want to put you through that."

I said nothing.

"This is no ordinary raid," Sgt. Donnelly continued. "This is another Profumo case." Then in a lowered voice he asked, "Is it true Jeb Richenbach was one of your johns?"

"No comment," I said.

"Celeste, we have the books and he is listed in one of your books," Sgt. Donnelly said.

"Some of those books were not mine," I said.

"If you don't give out a couple of big names, the D. A. is not going to get much publicity and then you'll be the loser."

"I'm not helping the D. A.," I said. Suddenly I was very tired. All I could think of was my family seeing me on the eleven o'clock news being escorted by two cops into the D. A.'s office. My mother would never get over it. When I thought of my life for the last two years I was filled with such shame and disgust, I wanted to die. And all the while my family had thought I was in show business.

"Would you give me the name of just one baseball player?" Sgt. Donnelly asked.

"What about my rights?" I asked. "Can't I call an attorney?"

"No one here is denying you your rights, Celeste. You can call an attorney later," he said.

I was getting so sleepy that I no longer heard the questions, just his voice. Suddenly I was jolted into fresh awareness as Sgt. McPherson started firing questions. "Celeste, tell us who was behind you."

"I told you before. No one was behind me," I said.

Another cop came into the room and said something to Sgt. McPherson I could not hear. Then Sgt. McPherson, leaning across the desk, said triumphantly, "Your friends, Lana and Tracy, have turned state's evidence against you!"

I knew this was a standard police tactic to get people to talk. "I don't believe you," I said.

"Where do your girls get their heroin?" he asked.

"I have no idea," I said.

"How much do they pay for it?"

"Why don't you ask them?"

"Your attitude isn't helping you," McPherson said.

I wondered how Lana and Melanie were holding up. They hadn't had a fix since early Friday afternoon. They must be in really bad shape.

"Melanie is the only girl who hasn't ratted you out," Sgt. McPherson said.

"Really?"

He banged his fist on the desk. "God damn you!" he shouted.

"Wait a minute, Mac," Sgt. Donnelly said. "Go easy on her." Then he spoke to me. "Celeste, won't you reconsider and give us a couple of big names? Then we can all go home."

"You can get the names from the D. A.," I said.

"You have to understand something, Celeste," Sgt. Donnelly said. "The D. A. cannot reveal any of the names of the johns to the press because if you denied it, he would be sued for libel and there would be a big scandal."

"I will not give out any names," I said flatly.

"If you will reveal just a few names, the judge will see to it that you do not go to prison," Sgt. Donnelly said.

"I don't care if I go to prison," I said.

"Celeste, I'm on your side," Sgt. Donnelly said gently. "I

don't want to see you do heavy time, but when your girls and johns testify against you, you will be facing big time."

"Don't you understand that because my family is ruined, nothing matters to me, not even going to prison!"

"And don't you understand," Sgt. McPherson shouted, "that you can't fight the D. A.'s office? This is the biggest case we've cracked in years. We've got you cold! And we are going to question you until you come up with the right answers!"

"If you have nothing better to do than try to get publicity for your boss, go right ahead and keep harassing me," I said.

"You damned hooker!" he shouted and left the office, slamming the door.

The blinding light was turned off and Sgt. Donnelly said, "Come on, Celeste. We're going to take you to the precinct in New York City."

As I was leaving I glanced at the large clock on the wall. It was 3 a.m. Melanie and Lana must be out of their heads by now.

In the hallway there was a group of reporters and photographers. When they saw me they started shouting questions. I paid no attention to them. I was watching for Melanie and Lana. Finally they came out of another room and I could not believe my eyes. Instead of crying and carrying on for a fix, they were both smiling!

Chapter XVII

Harassment

"Celeste, I hope you understand that Detective Donahue had to do this," Sgt. Donnelly said. "The district attorney is mounting his campaign and you are his stepping stone into the governor's mansion."

"I understand," I said. I understood too well. And nothing could heal the heartache of what Ray had done to me. Nothing could justify his treachery.

As for the D. A., I hated him and everyone connected with him. Within a short time the girls and I were in the precinct to be booked on the charge of prostitution. As we walked in I could hear the cops laughing. "They charged $100," one said. "I wouldn't give any of them ten bucks."

As we were being fingerprinted a cop said to Lana, "If you had me, Blondie, you'd give me my money back."

After the mug shots were taken the four of us were put in a large cell. I sat down on a cot and lowered my head. I wondered what condition my family was in. At first I was hardly aware of my girls, but later I realized that Lana and Tracy had been avoiding me since we arrived. Another thing—Lana and Melanie were not crying out for a fix. Tracy hadn't looked at me once. Lana was pacing back and

forth and had her back to me. When she turned in my
direction, she looked at me and her eyes filled with tears.
"Celeste, how come you ratted us out?" she asked.

"Lana, I never ratted any of you out," I said. "The police
told you that. They used the old psychology trick on you
to get you to talk."

"They used more than that," Melanie said, "but I still
didn't talk."

"What do you mean?" I asked, but I already knew.

"The cops gave me coke to make me talk, but I wouldn't,"
Melanie said.

"Thanks, Melanie," I said. "You've got guts."

Lana came over to me. "Celeste, forgive me. I had to
have a fix and they gave me coke." She began crying. "I'm
no good. I'm just a low-class junkie, a rat. I had to give
up my own baby because of drugs."

Tracy didn't have Lana's excuse for ratting me out. "Well,
we were all psyched," she said.

Melanie looked at her with loathing. It was the first time
I had ever seen such an expression on Melanie's face. I
couldn't be upset by what Tracy had done. By comparison
to everything else, it was minor. I stretched out on the cot.
I hadn't had any sleep since Thursday night. I hadn't had
a decent meal since Friday night. And since eight o'clock
Friday night when the raid had started, I'd been under con-
tinual harassment. I closed my eyes. I would have given
anything in the world to fall asleep. From the next cell I
could hear girls throwing up and crying out for a fix. I got
up and walked to the side of our cell. Two young girls were
lying across cots and there were abcessed quinine burns as
big as half dollars all over their legs. They cursed at the
guard every time she walked by.

I think you should get out while you can. Jane's words
came back to me. How I wished I had listened to her! I sat
down on the cot again and put my head in my hands. I
could never face Mother. I thought of the hell she'd been

through for years and years and yet she had given me all her love, all her time, never complaining, never thinking of herself. And in return I had destroyed her. I had ruined my entire family—Grandma, sisters, brother, nieces, nephews, aunts and uncles. "Oh, God!" I silently screamed. "Let me die!"

At 7 a.m. a policewoman brought us coffee and doughnuts. We were grateful for the steaming coffee but none of us could eat the doughnuts.

Just before 9 a.m. we were taken by the police to Prostitution Court at 100 Center Street, New York City. As we entered the courthouse we were met by a crowd of reporters and photographers. "Celeste, won't you give us a couple of big names? How about the assemblyman?" a reporter pleaded.

"Why don't you ask the D. A.?" I replied.

"Celeste, is it true an ambassador was one of your johns?" another reporter asked.

"No comment," I said.

When we were inside the courtroom it was 10 a.m. Judge Baylor spoke to us individually and each of us was charged with loitering for the purposes of prostitution. Bail for each was set at $500 cash. Then we were put in the bullpen.

"With all the publicity we're getting," Tracy said, "you'd think we'd committed murder."

"Or blown up a building or burned the flag," Lana said.

A couple of hours later Melanie looked sick. "Celeste, if I don't get a fix soon, I'll go crazy!" she said.

Lana was sweating. "I'm getting cramps," she said. "I've never gone without a fix. I hope we get out of here soon."

By three o'clock that afternoon Melanie and Lana were shuddering and had diarrhea. I remembered the time Melanie had tried to kick her habit with medication. Early that night she'd been out of her head.

At four o'clock we were escorted to a police car and driven

to the Women's House of Detention on Tenth Street, New York City. We immediately made bail and as we left the building, Melanie cried, "I have to have a fix fast!"

Lana was crying and shaking.

"I'm taking Lana to the club for a fix," Tracy said and hailed a cab.

"I'll go with you to the club, Melanie, and wait in the cab while you get a fix. Then we'll go some place where no one will know us," I said. I stepped toward the curb to hail a cab when two cops came over and re-arrested me, this time for procuring.

"My God!" I gasped in shock.

"Oh, no!" Melanie cried.

"Melanie, don't worry," I said. "I'll contact you at the club or at Tracy's when I get the chance."

I got into an unmarked police car with the cops. I was driven back to the district attorney's office. When I sat down in the waiting room it was 5:30 p.m. Minutes later I was taken into an office and once again interrogated by two detectives. Sergeant Doolittle shone a bright light in my face. "Celeste, we are not going to let up on you until you give us some names in organized crime that backed you," he said.

"No one backed me," I said. "You've been reading too many detective stories."

"Don't get smart with me," he said. "Why don't you tell the press the name of the assemblyman?"

"I don't know what you're talking about," I said.

He put a typewritten sheet of paper in front of me.

"Look, we know who it is. Just sign this statement and you can go home and get some sleep."

"I'm not signing anything," I said. I was so lightheaded and weak from lack of sleep and food, I started to cry.

"Come on, Celeste, I don't like to see you cry," Sergeant Ranada said. "If you'll give out a couple of big names, you won't have to worry about doing time."

He apparently thought I was crying about going to prison. He didn't know that the only thing I was thinking of was my family.

"Celeste, we seized the books on your johns. We've got the names. All we ask is that you give out a couple of names so we can get some publicity for the D.A. Then you'll be so big, you can write a book," Sgt. Doolittle said.

"Those aren't all my ledgers you seized," I said. Many of them weren't, but he'd never believe that. During the past two years I'd bought ledgers from prostitutes across the country, girls who were desperate for money.

"Then name your own damn johns!" he shouted. "Don't be so stubborn. You're only hurting yourself!"

I'm only hurting the D. A. I thought. And I planned to hurt him all I could. "Have you finished yet?" I asked.

Sgt. Doolittle brought his fist down on the desk. "You are the toughest dame I have ever met. But I have news for you. I'm a lot tougher than you are!"

I closed my eyes. Tired as I was, in some unfathomable way I was less tired than when I'd been questioned Friday night for all those hours. Now it was as though all feeling had been replaced by a numbness.

"Just give the press the name of that famous vocalist," Sgt. Doolittle said.

"Sorry," I said. "I don't seem to remember any names."

"You cheap hooker!" he shouted. "We'll get it out of you one way or another!" He got up and left the room. I could overhear him say to a cop in the hall, "I have broken men in six hours but this dame will not crack!"

I was questioned, badgered and harassed until four o'clock Sunday morning, a total of ten hours. Throughout the questioning I kept thinking of my mother. I could see her big sorrowful eyes and every now and then I broke down sobbing, but the detectives could not break me. And I was determined they would never break me.

"Come on, Celeste," Sgt. Ranada said, "We're going for a

little ride." He turned off the bright light and although I couldn't see his face clearly because the white glare was still in front of my eyes, I could hear real compassion in his voice. Sgt. Ranada and Sgt. Doolittle escorted me to an unmarked police car. I sat in the back and they sat up front. Within minutes we had left the main thoroughfare and were driving over back roads. I'd never seen this area before. It was run down and the roads were in disrepair, full of potholes. Sgt. Doolittle was driving and made no attempt to slow down for the wide pothole ahead. As he drove over it my head hit the ceiling of the car. He kept driving at the same speed, swerving the car and I began to feel dizzy. He hit another pothole and I was thrown forward. "My God! What are you doing?" I cried.

He smashed on the brakes and I was thrown forward again. He had almost hit the truck in front of us. Then, with tires screeching, he passed the truck and drove crazily down the road, hitting more potholes. I realized this was a psyche game to break me down. "Celeste, when you decide to cooperate we'll stop the car," Sgt. Doolittle said.

The car continued to bounce and lurch and I lay down on the back seat. It was safer and less frightening. As he continued to smash on the brakes, speed over potholes, jerk and swerve the car, I held onto the leather seat and cried silently. Hour after hour this went on, but I would not let on how much it bothered me.

"Celeste, if you'll cooperate with the D. A., you won't do a day in jail," Sgt. Ranada said.

I could tell he disliked being a part of this treatment. "I will never cooperate!" I said. "You are wasting your time. I know nothing. I am innocent!"

"In that case," Sgt. Doolittle said, "you will be going to prison for life."

Finally after five hours of being terrorized in the car, I was taken to the Supreme Court to be arraigned on felony charges. I spoke to the clerk of the court, identified myself and told him why I'd been arrested. "Can you recommend a good lawyer for me?" I asked.

Without hesitation he said, "Murray Rosenthal."

He put a call through for me and one hour later Mr. Rosenthal came into the courthouse. He took my hand. "Celeste, I can't tell you how honored I am to represent you!" He was treating me as though I were a celebrity.

Later we went into the courtroom before Judge Fineburg to be arraigned. After the preliminaries were over with, Judge Fineburg said, "Miss Clemente, you are charged with running a disorderly house. How do you plead, guilty or not guilty?"

"Not guilty," I said.

The assistant district attorney, Mr. O'Rourke, said, "Your honor, I recommend you set Miss Clemente's bail at ten thousand dollars because I have information that she might flee the country to jump bail."

I wanted to laugh. You would think I was a Communist spy.

The judge looked at me disdainfully. "I want you to know one thing, young lady. I hate prostitution. I am going to stamp it out of my county and I am going to do it with this case. And as long as I'm on the bench, you'll get the maximum sentence."

I tried to keep my face expressionless.

"Bail is set at five thousand dollars!" Judge Fineburg said. "Case adjourned until March 16 at 9:30 a.m."

When we were out in the hallway Mr. Rosenthal said, "Celeste, you have to raise $5,000 for bail. Do you know anyone who can come up with that figure today?"

"Yes," I said. "My mother will." Thank God I had been sending her large sums of money over the past two years.

I couldn't bear to think of seeing Mother. I had hoped never to have to face anyone in my family again, but now I had no choice. Mr. Rosenthal called Mother and an hour later Mother and Rita walked into the Supreme Court.

Mother's face was grey and stricken. She moved slowly and when she looked over at me, I rushed into her arms.

"My baby! My baby!" she cried. Her whole body was shaking and she was crying brokenly. I began sobbing. Finally I got control of myself and let go of her.

"Now, Mother, you have got to stop crying," I said. "Everything is going to be all right."

Mother continued sobbing and Rita put her arm around her. "Celeste, why didn't you contact us sooner?" Rita asked. "We have been frantic with worry."

I just looked at Rita without speaking. Mother was crying so hard that I couldn't think straight. "Mother, I have the best lawyer in New York," I said. "There's nothing to worry about."

"The paper says you might go to prison for life!" she cried. She was carrying on as though I were going to the electric chair.

"That's not true, Mother," I said.

"I don't know how you ever got involved in such a thing," she said. "I can't believe it. I just can't believe it!"

"It's all a set-up," I said. "The arrest was politically motivated." I laughed, hoping to reassure her.

Mr. Rosenthal came over to us and I introduced him. Mother calmed down a little and went through her pocketbook and handed him her bank book. "Good. I called a bailbondsman and he's here now," he said and walked off.

"Mother, it's not the end of the world," I said. "I'll be walking out of here in a few minutes with my attorney. And when everything is over with, you'll see I'll be free."

Mr. Rosenthal returned and the four of us walked out of the building. When we reached the bottom of the steps, Rita took me aside. "When I saw you on the eleven o'clock news Friday night, I rushed right over to the house. Mother and Dad had both collapsed and I took them to the emergency room. I thought they were going to have heart attacks, but they're all right." She put her arm around me.

"You know we're with you, Celeste, no matter what."

"Thanks, Rita," I said. The tears were coursing down my cheeks.

"Grandma doesn't know a thing," she said. "You know she and Grandpa don't own a TV and never look at the papers. Friday night I removed a tube from their radio and we'll see to it they don't find out through anyone else."

"Thanks, Rita," I said.

Rita and Mother left and I got in Murray Rosenthal's car and we drove to Manhattan. Minutes later I was sitting in Mr. Rosenthal's office. "I'm going to die if I don't get some sleep," I said.

"You better check into a hotel later," he said. "I don't want the police to know where you are. If you return to your apartment, you may find the police have planted a kilo of dope there. I don't want you to be a set-up."

"I hadn't even thought of that," I said.

"That's why you have me," he said. Mr. Rosenthal mixed a stiff drink for me. I swallowed it in gulps and within seconds I could feel myself relaxing.

"I have to go over a few facts with you," he said. He began asking questions and rapidly covered the highlights of the past two years. "There's one thing that concerns me," he said. "The money you put in the safe deposit box. It would be more secure in a savings account."

"I can't have a savings account," I said.

"In my name it would be safe," he said. "No one would know it was your money."

"I don't like the idea," I said.

"I'm just trying to be helpful," he said.

"I don't need that kind of help," I said. I wondered if there was a lawyer anywhere who would not try to take advantage of me.

Mr. Rosenthal leaned back in his chair. "I must be candid with you, Celeste," he said. "I'll do my best but you should know that with your record I can guarantee nothing."

"I wasn't born yesterday, Mr. Rosenthal."

"I need five thousand down," he said, "and remember, there are no guarantees."

I agreed to the price.

"Tomorrow, Celeste, I want you back here at 1:30 and I'll go over the whole thing carefully."

"Fine," I said. "Now I can get some sleep."

"I've arranged a press conference," he said. "The reporters will be here in a few minutes."

"What?" I cried. "After all I've been through? Three days and nights of harassment from the cops, the press hounding me at every turn, no sleep since last Thursday, and you've called a press conference?"

"Calm down, Celeste, This is the best thing for you. So far all the publicity has been detrimental. Now I can start winning sympathy for you if you'll cooperate."

I glared at him.

"You are not the typical middle-aged, hard madam," he said. "You are a beautiful young girl."

"Oh, all right," I said.

"You admit nothing to the press," he said. "You are innocent."

I nodded.

"Do you have any of the stories that were in the papers?" I asked.

He pointed to a stack of papers on his desk and handed one to me. "You made the front page of the *Daily News* and you're in every paper in town, plus many across the country."

I read quickly. "Thirty-Nine Probers Hunt Steerers in $250,000 Vice Ring." I scanned the article. The district attorney yesterday threw thirty investigators into the intensive search for steerers for a $250,000-a-year vice ring that drew part of its clientele from Long Island's Jet Set...underworld connections in the vice set...Andrews said he has five assistant district attorneys and fifteen county detectives in his office, plus seventeen detectives and two policewomen from the district attorney's police squad working around the clock on the case. They are particularly concerned with the procurers, located in swank restaurants and hotels, according to Jones...Andrews said his probers have gone without sleep for the past seventy-two hours. Some sixteen ledgers and books with names of two hundred johns...were seized in the raid Friday night. Jones said the ring has been under scrutiny for six months."

I read the article in the Sunday *News*. The banner headline was, "Vice Jills Got Jack from Bigwig Johns." There was a front page article in the Sunday *Long Island Press*. "Vice Ring Ledgers Name 'Customers' on Four Continents" was the headline.

Many of the news stories mentioned that the investigation of the murder of Joe Rizzo had been linked to me but I'd been proven clean of any connection with the Mafia and the murders.

"The district attorney has built me up to look like the most notorious madam in history!" I said. "By comparison, Polly Adler looks like Minnie Mouse!"

"Now look, Celeste," Mr. Rosenthal said, "I'm going to give it to you straight. This is the biggest story since the assassination of John Kennedy. We're all going to cash in on it. If you're smart this could be the start of the biggest thing in your life. If you cooperate with me you'll be getting offers from magazines to do a story on you, maybe even a movie contract. You can become a millionaire. We just have to sit tight and wait until this election is over. After the election we won't have any trouble from the D. A."

"I'm not cashing in on it," I said. "My family is suffering enough. I'm not going to make it any worse for them."

"You've been through a lot," he said, "but the worst is over."

He was so wrong. The worst was still going on. My family was falling apart from shock and heartache and no amount of time was ever going to ease the pain for them.

In the next moment the reporters and photographers burst into the office. As the reporters started firing questions, a photographer was snapping one picture after the other. "Celeste, is it true a major league ball player was one of your johns? What was his name?" one reporter asked.

"I don't know what you're talking about," I said.

"Celeste, will you give us the name of the famous philanthropist?" another reporter asked.

"I have no information for you," I said. "I am innocent. I have been framed!"

Chapter XVIII

The Publicity

I reached Melanie at Tracy's apartment. "Meet me at the little place on Third Avenue," I said. "I'll be there in ten minutes."

"Will do," she said and hung up.

At least I had one friend left I could count on, one friend I could talk to.

When Melanie walked into the lounge I quickly brought her up-to-date on everything. I told her about the ten additional hours of interrogation yesterday and the five hours of being terrorized in the police car.

"You're the vice queen," she said. "One of the cops told me they're out to break you. You're the publicity for the D. A. I haven't been subjected to any harassment. They're not interested in me. As far as the D. A. is concerned, I'm just another hooker."

"Well, they'll never break me," I said. "If I don't give out any big names, all of the D. A.'s work for the past six months will have been for nothing!"

"Where are we going to stay?" Melanie asked. "My attorney, Mr. Coughlin, told me it wouldn't be safe to go back to our apartment."

"My attorney told me the same thing," I said. "We'll go

to a hotel."

"I've never been so tired in my life," Melanie said.

"I'm dead myself," I said. "Come on, let's go. "

A few minutes later we were in a hotel room. "I've got to be in Rosenthal's office tomorrow at 1:30," I said.

"I'll call you," Melanie said. "Don't worry about it."

I collapsed on the bed and never remembered falling asleep. The next thing I knew Melanie was tugging at my arm. "Celeste, get up. It's noon time," she said.

I got out of bed and stared at her. "How come you look so good?" I asked.

"I had my fix," she said.

I marveled that even in the midst of these charges Melanie's only concern was her habit.

As I left the room I said, "I'll meet you later at that lounge on Third Avenue."

"Okay," she said. "See you."

When I arrived at Rosenthal's office the first thing he said was, "Celeste, you don't look well. When was the last time you had a good meal?"

"Friday night," I said.

"Well, this is Monday," he said. "You've got to start eating." He dialed a number and ordered a chicken dinner for me. Then he pushed a button on the intercom and asked his secretary to buy a copy of every New York City newspaper.

Minutes later a boy came in with the food and as I ate the chicken, I began to feel stronger. The secretary returned with the newspapers and as Rosenthal scanned one paper, he broke into a broad grin. "Celeste, you made the centerfold of the *Daily News!*" he said.

I looked at the paper on his desk and there was a picture of me with Rosenthal taken yesterday in his office. He was still looking at the picture, still smiling, and with a sinking feeling I realized he was enjoying the publicity for himself.

I read through the sensational account and remembered

that my father walked to the paper store every day and bought the *Daily News*. I glanced again at the sexy picture. Mother would be sick when she saw it. I read the stories in the other city papers. "A national emergency wouldn't get this much coverage," I said.

"That's politics," Rosenthal said.

He summoned his secretary again and began questioning me. She took everything down in shorthand as he went over all of the activities of my life for the past two years. When he was through his secretary left and he began explaining the law to me. "Prostitution is a misdemeanor," he said, "punishable usually by six months in jail. Procuring is a felony with a mandatory sentence of five years."

"How much time will I do?" I asked.

"It looks bad," he said, "because of the great number of girls you had working for you and because you had so many johns. Your sentence will depend upon how many people testify against you."

"I'm doomed," I said.

"I have to be honest with you. The D. A. won't have any trouble getting people to testify. The girls will be given immunity if they testify. You'll get five years for each one who talks, so if only ten people testify that's fifty years right there."

"I'm not looking for a miracle," I said. "I know I'm going to do heavy time."

Rosenthal took out a decanter of Scotch and mixed a drink for me.

"Melanie is the only friend I have now," I said. "She's the only one who didn't rat me out.

"I know," he said. "And she'll do time because of it."

"When will I go to trial?"

"That's anyone's guess," he said. "The D. A. wants all the publicity he can get so you can be sure this case will be dragged out." He smiled suddenly. "Celeste, I've heard a lot of the big names through the grapevine. Tell me about the politicians."

I gave him names of johns from Washington, congress-men from many states, and with each name, he slapped his knee, threw back his head and roared. When I told him I'd gone with Peter Finchley, his eyes popped.

"I don't believe it!" he said.

"Peter was not a john," I said. "I never took any money from him. Peter was in love with me. He wanted to marry me."

"What?" He stared at me in disbelief.

"Oh, yes," I said. "I saw Peter many times. We went to Bermuda together. He is a very pathetic man."

"My God, why didn't you marry him?"

"I didn't love him."

"You didn't love him! With all his millions, love would matter?"

"Believe it or not, love was what mattered most to me. I was always looking for Prince Charming."

I told Mr. Rosenthal about the johns from the Jet Set, the nationally known sports figures, stars of stage and screen. "I could tell you about a john you know personally through your work," I said.

"Who?" His eyes were bulging.

"Roland Barbaro."

"What? I can't believe it!" He roared laughing. "What turned Barbaro on?"

"He likes everyone, including young boys," I said.

"This is too much!" He stood up and started walking back and forth, shaking his head and laughing.

It was almost three o'clock and I wanted to get my clothes. "Would it be all right to go to the apartment just one time to pick up my clothes?"

"If you go in daylight with Melanie and leave immediately, it might be all right," he said.

As I stood up he said, "Celeste, I've scheduled a press conference for three o'clock."

"What?" I was furious.

"I explained yesterday that this coverage will help you. Be realistic and cooperate."

"I guess at this point it doesn't make any difference," I said. "We're still making radio news every fifteen minutes. The way they're carrying on about us, you'd think little green men had landed from Mars."

A few minutes later the room was full of reporters and a couple of photographers were shooting film as we talked. Through the din of voices a young reporter sprang forward. "Celeste, is it true you were making $250,000 a year?"

"I don't know what you're talking about," I said.

Another reporter asked, "Celeste, will you please give us a couple of johns from the *Social Register*?"

"I really have nothing to tell you people," I said. I was getting annoyed. I resented Rosenthal for calling this press conference, especially without telling me first. The reporters were disappointed with my answers and soon left.

"The district attorney wants you to reveal names to the press to prove that this is a sensational story," Rosenthal said.

"Whose side are you on?" I asked.

"I'm on your side, of course. Celeste, believe me, it would be better for you—the judge will go easy on you— if you give some names to the press."

"Well, I won't. And that's final," I said. "I've disgraced my family enough." I walked out of his office without another word. Every time I thought of the district attorney, my blood boiled.

I met Melanie at the lounge and after we had a couple of drinks we drove to our old apartment building. When we arrived on the sixteenth floor there was a sign on our door. "This is a raided premise. Owners may claim their property at the county dump." It was signed by the sheriff. I still had a key and we went inside. The place had been stripped bare. We drove to the dump and claimed our clothing and the oil paintings. Later we went out for a drink near the hotel. "When this is all over," Melanie said, "I'm going to lead a normal life."

"What are you going to do?"

"I'm going to business school. Then I'm going to get a job as a secretary in a big corporation."

"That sounds like a good idea," I said, though I wondered how Melanie was going to kick her habit. And if she survived the withdrawal, would she survive life in prison?

When we were back in our room we stayed up drinking and smoking pot. "Celeste, let's get out of this hotel room," Melanie said. "It's depressing. Couldn't we visit your family tomorrow?"

"Oh, Melanie, after that scene in the courthouse yesterday, I dread seeing Mother again."

"Your mother will suffer more if she doesn't see you."

What she said was true. And there was nothing I wanted more than to go home and have Mother greet me with a big happy smile the way she used to. But those days were gone forever. "Maybe by the end of the week we'll visit," I said.

By 2 a.m. we'd finished a fifth of whiskey and I went to bed.

For the rest of the week all we did was read the newspaper accounts about us, drink and smoke pot. The story had been carried on the wire services overseas. At times I felt as though all of this was not really happening to me. Since the story broke I hadn't heard from any of my friends. The worst part was Ray. I still could not believe what he had done to me. And to think that I had expected to marry him. I had even let myself dream about having my own little baby.

Friday afternoon we drove to my home and when Mother opened the door, she cried out, "My baby!" She held me in her arms. Melanie had been right. I would have been cruel to stay away from Mother.

Mother kissed Melanie. "You're always welcome, honey,"

she said.

When we walked into the living room I couldn't believe the tableau that greeted my eyes. The curtains were drawn and the room was dark. My father was sitting in his chair, slumped over and four of his friends from Italy, the Petrucellis and the Schipanis, were sitting on the couch dressed in black. It looked exactly like a wake. When Dad saw me, he said, "Celeste, how coulda youa doa thisa toa mea?" Tears were streaming down his face.

"Dad, it's going to be all right," I said.

"Whata maken youa becomea a girla likea thisa?"

I'd never seen my father cry.

"Whata disgracea!" he said.

"Yes, you certainly disgraced your nicea Italiana family," Mr. Petrucelli said. His wife was crying. Mr. and Mrs. Schipani wouldn't look at me but stared straight ahead.

Mother and Melanie had gone into the kitchen. I started to follow them and I heard Dad say, "You' worsa thana deada!"

"Don't be upset, Celeste," Mother said. "It's hard on your father. When he goes to the store, the kids throw rocks at him. I've told him not to go but he won't listen."

"Mother, if you don't mind, I think we'd better go to Rita's."

"I understand," she said, "but come back in a few days. Dad won't be carrying on like this for long."

Rita and Artie were very kind to us and we stayed for dinner. Later in the kitchen I helped Rita clean up. "Kids have been throwing rocks at our house," she said. "At Vera's and Marilyn's too. But the worst part is what's happening to our children. The kids in school are taunting them."

"Oh, God!" I cried. "I'm sorry, Rita!"

Later we went into the living room and had coffee. Rita insisted that I repeat the entire story of the raid for Artie and I noticed that she hung on every word as if she were hearing it for the first time. All this publicity was turning her on.

"I don't know how you have survived all this," Artie said.

"If I didn't get high every night, I wouldn't be here to talk about it," I said.

"Oh, Celeste will come through," Rita said. "It will all work out, you'll see."

"I hope so," Artie said, but it was obvious he didn't think it would.

"The hardest part is what it's doing to Mother," I said.

"Yeah, she's in pretty bad shape," Rita said. "She was getting so many obscene telephone calls, we had the number changed."

"Celeste doesn't need to hear about that," Artie said.

Rita disregarded him and went on in the same vein. "Every morning when Dad picks up the News someone says something. One guy said to him, 'I'd like to go to bed with your daughter. How much does she charge?'"

I couldn't believe anyone could be that cruel.

"Now Dad's drinking more than ever, but he still won't admit he's been an alcoholic for forty years," she said, laughing.

"I used to feel sorry for myself," Melanie said, "but now I think I'm better off than Celeste. At least no one is heartbroken over me."

The doorbell rang and my brother Chris walked in. When he saw me, his face hardened. "You have ruined everyone in this family!" he said.

"Chris, you don't understand," I said. "This is a political bust."

"I understand one thing," he said. "Your real name was in the papers. I am raising a son and a daughter and they have to carry that name with them for the rest of their lives. You have ruined our family name and almost killed your father!"

He turned and was about to leave the house. I stood up

and shouted, "My father should have thought of that when he came home drunk every night when I was a kid. All this talk about Dad! I'm the one facing life. Don't you care about me?" He slammed the door and was gone.

Melanie and I left right after him. "We never should have gone to see them," I said.

"It was only your brother who gave you a hard time," she said.

"And my father and his friends," I said.

Melanie didn't say anything more on the subject. When we were back in the hotel room we drank and smoked pot. Later when I got into bed I prayed. "Oh, God, take my life," I said. "Even if I go to hell, it's better than being here!"

Two weeks went by and I had to go to Rosenthal's office again. "Your old friend Barbaro was fired yesterday," he said, chuckling.

"Why?"

"The D. A. saw his name in one of your books and mentioned it to me. I confirmed that Barbaro was a john so the D. A. fired him."

"But I didn't give his name to the press."

"You have to understand that the D. A. thought, quite naturally, you were going to reveal Barbaro's name to the press, so in order to protect himself, he had to fire him."

"Did it get in the papers?"

"No, and it won't. You can count on that," Rosenthal said. "Anyhow, next week we go to court. I want to go over everything with you now." He explained the legalities involved, which he'd already explained to me before. He reviewed the pertinent facts and prepared me for every eventuality.

"When is all this going to end?" I asked.

"You have to be patient, Celeste," he said. "The D. A. is going to keep this case going for as long as he can."

"The D. A.!" I said. "One man's ambition is ruining the lives of everyone I care about!"

The following week I went to court and as it turned out, it was a waste of time. Judge Fineburg kept eyeing my mink coat. "This case has to be brought to trial as soon as possible," he said. "I want this woman off the streets. I want her convicted and imprisoned."

Later in his office Mr. Rosenthal said, "Celeste, don't be despondent. You've got to make up your mind to the fact that this could go on for a long time. You've got to change your attitude or you could have a breakdown."

"I don't even care about the case," I said. "It's my family and. . ." I didn't finish. I couldn't talk to him about Ray.

"Incidentally, the reason the judge was so nasty to you today was because he thought you were responsible for Barbaro being fired. Barbaro is well liked in legal circles, very well liked and respected."

I wondered what the judges and lawyers would think of Barbaro if they knew what a degenerate he was.

"Well, now if you'll give me $1,000 to cover costs for the past two weeks," he said.

I was shocked. I'd already paid him $5,000 a month ago, the first time I'd seen him. Nevertheless, without arguing, I agreed to pay the additional $1,000.

"I've scheduled a press conference for one o'clock," he said.

"Oh, my God!" I cried.

"It's only for a few minutes," he said. "Celeste, I am very serious when I say that I wish you would reconsider and give a few names to the press."

"Otherwise," I said, "the D. A.'s efforts for the past seven months will have been for nothing!"

"Oh, come on, Celeste. I'm thinking of your welfare!"

A few minutes later the office was crowded with reporters and photographers. A reporter with a nasal voice said, "Celeste, there have been numerous accounts in the papers, stating that an undercover man from the D. A.'s office has been given most of the credit for breaking this prostitution ring. Would you care to comment on that?"

"Yes," I said, avoiding Rosenthal's attempt to silence me with his eyes. "That undercover man was my boyfriend."

The room erupted into pandemonium with all the reporters shouting at once. "Would you elaborate on that statement?" another reporter asked, his eyes popping.

"I was in love with that man," I said, ignoring Rosenthal, who was now standing next to me, telling me to keep still. "He was not a john. I never accepted money from him. We had an honest relationship. I was in love with him right from the start and I thought. . . ." My voice faltered. "I thought he was in love with me."

"That's enough boys!" Rosenthal barked.

"Would you give us the name of that undercover man?" the reporter asked.

Rosenthal opened the door for them to leave and I said, "His name is Detective Ray Donahue."

"Come on, boys, break it up!" Rosenthal shouted.

"How do you feel about Detective Donahue now?" a reporter asked.

"I have no hard feelings," I said.

"Come on, Celeste, you must be bitter," he said.

"Bitter? I'm not bitter," I said. "I'll love Ray Donahue until the day I die!"

Chapter XIX
I'd Rather Be Dead

Melanie and I were drinking in our hotel room when the phone rang at nine o'clock. "Now, who could that be?" she asked.

I picked up the receiver. It was Nick Valentino. "Nick, how did you know where I was staying?" I asked. Immediately I realized it was a foolish question.

"I have my ways," he laughed. "You know that, Celeste."

"Yeah, Nick," I said and laughed.

"I'm sorry about the bust you took," he said. "It's a shame. Could you use a night out on the town?"

"I sure could!"

"I'll pick you up at ten tonight," he said.

When I hung up I felt better. Nick was always good for laughs, although I could never really relax in his company.

"Well, at least you've got one friend left besides me," Melanie said.

"You know why no one has tried to contact us, honey. They think I'm being tailed and they don't want any trouble. Let's face it. The heat is on and every prostitute has left town until this thing dies down."

"You're right," she said.

At ten o'clock I was down in the lobby, waiting for Nick. We went to a nightclub owned by a mobster.

When we were seated at a table, Nick said, "You're still the most beautiful broad I know. But you have lost weight."

"I've been eating less and drinking more," I laughed.

"And where you're going, you won't get anything to drink."

"I don't want to think about it," I said.

"It's a shame, a beautiful young girl like you," he said.

"How is Natalie?" I asked.

"She's fine. We're going to be married next month."

"I'm glad. She really loves you," I said.

"Natalie's the best," he said, "true blue."

Two men came over to our table and Nick asked them to have a drink. Benny and Rocco sat down and when Nick told them who I was they were all questions.

"It's rumored some of your johns were big politicians," Rocco said. "Is it true?"

"The papers said you had johns from the Jet Set," Benny said. "Could you give us some names, Celeste?"

"You're as bad as the reporters," I said.

Benny and Rocco went to the bar and Nick and I got up and danced. After a couple of hours of drinking and laughing I was able to forget the past weeks. Later we went to a motel and Nick gave me a hundred dollars. When he dropped me off at the hotel he said, "How about next Tuesday at seven o'clock?"

"Sure," I said, "if I'm not in jail."

The next day I had an appointment with Rosenthal. When I walked into the waiting room I heard him on the phone. "What do you want me to ask her? About which john?" He laughed. "Oh, you're a rip! I think she said he only likes black girls!" He roared laughing.

I walked straight into his office and he cut short his conversation. "Celeste, don't look so upset. Some day this will all be over," he said.

"That's not what I'm upset about," I said. "All along you've been trying to make a deal with the D. A. You've pressured me to give names to the press. You want publicity as much as the D. A. does."

"That's not true, Celeste."

"If this continues, I'll have to get another lawyer."

"Oh, don't do that!" His eyes were pleading. "I have your interests at heart, believe me."

He smiled suddenly. "Celeste, I received a telegram from a movie producer," he said and handed it to me.

I read it quickly. They wanted to make a movie about my life. There were conditions, however. I would have to name names. They quoted an astronomical sum of money they would pay.

"I'm not interested," I said, dropping the telegram on his desk.

"Celeste, you could make a fortune!"

"Is that all you wanted to see me about? How much longer is this going to go on?" I asked. "It's been over a month already."

"The D. A. is trying to get more of your johns and girls to sign statements against you. Each statement is a felony or five years. And, of course, the girls who testify will get immunity."

"You don't have to be a mathematical genius to know I'll be facing life."

"If you change your mind and give a couple of names to the press, you won't do a day in prison."

"I'm not putting my family through any more heartache."

"Okay, it's your neck," he said.

That night I met Melanie in a Chinese restaurant for dinner. "I'd almost rather be in prison than go on like this," I said, "never knowing what's going to happen next, not knowing how many times I'll have to go to court."

"I dread what will happen to me when I go to prison and have to kick my habit cold turkey," Melanie said.

"Don't worry about it until the time comes," I said. "It's best to take one day at a time. I never look past today. If I did, I'd lose my mind."

"Friday is my trial," she said.

"I'll be there," I said. "You can count on that."

I had expected Melanie would break down Thursday night but she smoked pot and drank and seemed resigned. She wasn't concerned about the trial or going to prison. Kicking her habit was her only concern.

At 9:15 the next morning we were in New York Prostitution Court. The trial finally got under way and Mr. Coughlin, her attorney, said, "Your honor, I would like the court to take into consideration all of the facts of this case. Miss Morrison has had no previous arrest. She is only twenty-one years old and the reason she got into prostitution was to support her drug habit. Your honor, my client has had an unfortunate background. When she left home at the age of sixteen, neither of her parents made any effort to locate her then or at any time since then."

"This court is not without heart," Judge Baylor said. "We are not here to persecute your client, Mr. Coughlin."

When the assistant D. A., Mr. Neuhauser, finished with his summation, the judge said, "This court finds the defendant, Miss Melanie Morrison, guilty of prostitution. Case adjourned until 9:30 a.m., April 21 for sentencing. Bail continued. Next case."

We went directly back to the hotel room and I mixed drinks for us. "Melanie, you're going to make it," I said.

"I still have to do time. I still have to kick my habit."

"You'll get a light sentence. The judge isn't down on you. He had to find you guilty because of all the publicity. And you'll be able to kick your habit. You're young and strong. You'll come through."

"It doesn't really matter that much what happens to

me," she said without rancor.

The following Tuesday afternoon Rosenthal called. "The indictments will be handed down Friday," he said. "I want you in my office at eight o'clock."

"Okay," I said and hung up.

When I told Melanie she said, "It will be a relief to get it over with."

"I don't know," I said. "It's one thing dreading it, but it's another thing having it spelled out."

I poured myself a double Scotch. "Actually, the indictments are just a formality," I continued. "Whether the case is dragged out for months or years, I'll be convicted and go to prison for the rest of my life."

The anger and bitterness, which had held me together during the past weeks was gone and now I was losing my tight control. "Oh, God, I wish I were dead!" I cried.

"Oh, Celeste, I wish I could help you!" Melanie cried.

"No one can help me now," I said and began sobbing.

Melanie handed me another drink. "And to think this is all Mr. Nice Guy's fault," she said. "If it hadn't been for him, you might never have been caught!"

When I thought of Ray and all the months of tender love scenes, it was more than I could bear.

"You may not go to trial for many months," Melanie said. "You may not go to prison for a couple of years."

"I'd just as soon go now. What am I going to do for the months ahead while the D. A. plays games with me?"

"Maybe you'll go to trial soon and be in prison in a few months," she said.

"Oh, what the hell difference does it make?" I cried. "My life is over!"

I poured more Scotch into the glass and the more I drank, the more I cried. After a couple of hours I began to feel sleepy. The next thing I knew Melanie was tugging on my arm. I opened my eyes. "What time is it?" I asked.

"It's 6 p.m.," she said.

I got out of the chair and poured myself a drink. Then I went to the phone. "Melanie, I'm calling room service for a sandwich. What would you like?"

"Celeste, you have a date tonight with Nick," she said. "This is Tuesday night."

"Oh, God!" I said. "I completely forgot. I can't go out with him now. I'm too depressed. I can't see anyone."

"It would be good for you to get out," she said. "You might even have a good time."

"A good time? You know, Melanie, sometimes I wonder about you."

"Well, what are you going to do between now and when you go to prison—lay down and die? It could be a long time."

"You're right. It could be a very long time," I said. "Okay, I'll see him."

I showered and put on a beautiful pale blue cocktail sheath. I wore my diamond necklace and took my ermine stole.

At seven o'clock I was downstairs in the lobby, watching for Nick. When I saw his black Cadillac pull up I went out to meet him. He opened the door and his face was drawn. I'd never seen him look tense or troubled, only angry on occasion. "What's the matter, Nick?" I asked. He must be in trouble with the Mob, I thought.

"You, that's what's the matter," he said as we pulled away from the curb.

My heart started pounding. We drove a few blocks in silence and then he said, "Celeste, you told Natalie about us."

"What are you talking about?" I cried. "I haven't seen Natalie for months!"

"She called me last night and said she found out about us."

"I would never tell her I'd been with you. I'd have to be crazy to do a thing like that!"

"Don't lie to me, Celeste!" he said. "You ruined the best thing that ever happened to me. Natalie is a raving maniac. She broke our engagement last night."

Nick would kill someone who even looked at him the wrong way. I was speechless. I never should have gotten mixed up with him. From the first time I laid eyes on him, I was afraid of him. He turned at the next corner and drove back to the hotel. Without another word he dropped me off.

I knew he might have someone waiting for me so I ran into the hotel and across the lobby to the elevators. I could feel my heart pounding in my ears as I waited for the elevator. When I reached the sixth floor I rushed into our room and leaned against the door trying to catch my breath.

"What happened?" Melanie cried.

"Nick thinks I told Natalie we'd been together. She broke their engagement."

"My God! He might knock you off for that!"

I poured myself a drink. "Don't open the door for anyone. Nick has his boys and he will know every move we make."

"Oh, let's get out of this place," Melanie said. "Let's go to your family."

"No, that's out," I said. "We might never make it there and even if we did, I don't want to involve them in anything else."

We drank the rest of the night. The next afternoon while we were having coffee Melanie said, "This hotel room is getting to me. You can't even get a decent meal here. Let's go out for dinner tonight."

"Okay," I said. "Actually, if the Mob killed me, they'd be doing me a favor."

"Celeste, don't talk like that! You know you don't mean it!"

"I mean it from the bottom of my heart," I said.

At six o'clock that night Melanie and I walked out of the hotel. It was a balmy night in April and there were a lot of people on the street. We were one block from the hotel when I spotted Nick standing on the corner with Benny and Rocco. I knew they were going to follow us. "Melanie, we've got to get back to the hotel fast," I said.

In two minutes we were back in our room. Fifteen minutes later there was a loud knock on the door. "Celeste, it's Rocco. Open up."

"I can't open the door, Rocco," I said. "You'd better leave. We just got tipped off that this whole place is bugged and the cops know where I am."

Without another word he left.

The next afternoon as we were talking in our room, Melanie smiled suddenly. "Celeste, I have the solution to all our problems!"

I looked at her in amazement.

"We can jump bail," she said. "We can go to Mexico and start a whole new life!"

"Melanie, I could not start a new life anywhere in the world. I am finished. I am through with prostitution. I am through with everything."

"Oh, Celeste, don't talk like that," she said. "You make it sound like I'm never going to see you again."

"I wish it would all end," I said. "I wish there was some way out!"

I mixed a Scotch and soda and for the rest of the afternoon I sat in the chair by the window, drinking. Melanie kept trying to draw me out but I ignored her. That evening Rita called. "Celeste, why haven't you been out to see us?" she asked.

"I'm not up to it," I said. "Now if you don't mind, Rita, I want to get off the phone."

"What am I going to tell Mother? She's carrying on worse than ever. Don't you see that be staying away, you're making things harder for her?"

"I don't care," I said. "I just don't care."

"I don't like the way you're talking," she said.

"There's nothing I can do about that."

"Well, I'll see you in court tomorrow," she said. "I love you, Celeste. We all love you, remember that."

I hung up the receiver, went to my room and threw myself on the bed. "Oh, God, how could I have done such a thing to my family?" I cried.

I beat my fists into the pillow and started sobbing. I was vaguely aware of Melanie standing over me. I cried until I was exhausted. Then I lay there very still.

Melanie brought in a tray. "I won't leave until you eat something," she said.

I looked at her. She was so beautiful and so easily hurt. "I'm sorry for the way I've been carrying on," I said.

"I understand," she said. "You don't have to apologize."

"You're a good friend," I said.

"You're the one who's the good friend," she said. "If it hadn't been for you I would have been hustling in the streets long ago."

To please Melanie I ate the sandwich. For the rest of the evening I was silent and subdued. That long, hard cry had drained me of everything.

When I went to bed that night I filled a glass with Scotch and put it on the nighttable. I got under the blankets and turned the light off. Tomorrow the indictments would be handed down. I began sipping the Scotch. I looked back over the last two years of my life. I'd made so many friends, helped so many young girls and they'd all ratted me out, all of them except Melanie. But that was nothing compared to what Ray had done. Ray had been my life, my very breath, my Prince Charming, the solution to all my problems. I would never get over what he had done to me. I thought of my family. My brother's words still burned in my ears. "You have ruined everyone in this family!" I could never forgive myself for the sorrow and shame I'd brought upon my family. But it was Mother with her loving eyes and broken heart that tore me apart. There was one good thing though—Grandma didn't know anything. Suddenly I recalled that day in Grandma's kitchen years ago when she had told me the story of Shadrach, Meshach, and Abednego. Even though they were cast bound into a fiery furnace, not a hair on their heads had been singed because Jesus had been with them. Grandma's words, repeated so often through the years came back. "Remember, Celeste, no matter what happens, Jesus will never leave you nor forsake you!"

Well, not even God could rectify my life now. Not even God could mend my family's broken hearts. I started to pray. "Oh, God, I'm sorry for every sin of my life!" I said. "Forgive me!"

With those words, the years I'd gone to church with Grandma flashed before my eyes, years of love and joy in the Lord. Scalding tears began to roll down my cheeks and I wondered how, after all the prayers and all the dreams of my childhood, I could have reached this point in my life.

Chapter XX

"I Will Never Leave Thee, Nor Forsake Thee."

The alarm went off at seven o'clock. I had a headache and my mouth and throat were dry. Worse, there was a heaviness throughout my body I'd never felt before.

"Hurry up, Celeste!" Melanie was wide awake and getting ready.

The first thing I did was take two bennys. After I was dressed and made up, I opened the medicine cabinet and took out the bottle of sleeping capsules and put it in my bag. Just before leaving the hotel room, Melanie and I had a stiff drink.

In Rosenthal's office I had to listen to him explain various points of law he'd already explained many times before. "You've got to be prepared for the worst, Celeste," he said. "Many of your girls have signed statements against you, stating you were their madam. As you know, they received immunity for turning State's evidence."

"So what else is new?"

"That's not all," he said. "The district attorney's boys threatened a number of johns, saying they would tell their wives if they didn't cooperate. The guys were scared and many of them signed statements against you. You must understand, Celeste, that when this case goes to trial you could be facing life."

"No!" I said. "As if I didn't know!"

I glanced at Melanie. She was pale and her lower lip was trembling. For the first time I realized how my case was tearing her apart.

"Let's go," Rosenthal said.

We went outside and Melanie and I got in my car and followed him to the Supreme Court. Inside the courthouse Rosenthal stopped in the hall to speak to another attorney. Melanie and I walked toward the courtroom and sat down on a bench. I noticed that the two guards standing outside the courtroom were staring at me. Then in a voice raised loud enough for me to hear, one of them said, "I hope she gets the chair for ratting out Barbaro!"

Melanie glanced at me nervously.

"Ignore them," I said.

Mr. O'Rourke was walking down the hallway toward us. He stopped in front of me. "You don't stand a chance," he said. "No matter what happens, you're getting life."

He left quickly and continued on his way to the other end of the hall. A group of reporters and two photographers came out of the elevator with Rita getting off last. She raced over to us. "Don't worry, Celeste," she said. "Somehow, things are going to work out."

Rita meant well and I was glad she was always around when I needed someone from my family, but even Rita knew things were not going to work out.

A young reporter was approaching us.

"Let's go," I said to Melanie and we stood up.

"Hi Celeste," the reporter said. "How do you feel this morning?"

When I ignored him, he said, "Cat got your tongue?"

Melanie and I walked quickly toward Rosenthal with the reporter right behind us. When Rosenthal saw us, he left the other attorney. "Not now, kid," he said to the reporter. "After court."

It was nine-thirty and we went into the courtroom. Rosenthal and I sat up front at the witness table. A number of strangers, curious about the indictments, had come to court and the room was filling up fast.

I knew I would have to stand with Rosenthal before the judge when the clerk read the indictments. As the judge conferred with O'Rourke, I reached in my bag and unscrewed the top of the bottle of sleeping capsules. I'd learned long ago how to swallow capsules without water. I shook a handful of them into my right hand and with my left hand I took out a few tissues and pretended to be blowing my nose. As I held the tissues over my nose and mouth with one hand, I slipped the capsules into my mouth with the other hand.

"The defendant will please rise," the clerk said. Rosenthal and I stood in front of Judge Fineburg.

The clerk began reading in a flat voice. "The State of New York versus Miss Celeste Clemente. The state charges the defendant with procuring for the purposes of prostitution. . . ." I was only half listening. It would be a long and boring recitation. Rosenthal had told me that. ". . .living off the proceeds of prostitute Lana Waring." Countless names of my girls were ticked off—Tracy McNulty, Etran Lin, Marta Olsen, Hilda Weinberger, Judy Wilson. I wondered where they got her name. She'd worked for me one week two years ago. The clerk's voice droned on and on as he read through the thick sheaf of papers in his hands. I glanced at the clock on the wall. It was ten o'clock and he'd been reading almost fifteen minutes. I wondered when he would stop. I was beginning to feel strange. "The State of New York charges Miss Celeste Clemente with twenty-seven felonies and ten misdemeanors," he said.

"Oh, my God!" Rita cried out.

The judge banged his gavel. "Order in the court!" he said.

The judge was looking at me, but I couldn't see him clearly.

"This case is adjourned until May 8 at 9:30 a.m..." His voice was receding. "Bail continued."

I made an effort to see his face, but now all I could see was his hair and eyes. He had no face. The next thing I knew I was on the floor, but I didn't remember falling. I heard Melanie's high thin cry and a woman yelled, "Someone get an ambulance!" People were peering down at me and the voice of that young reporter kept asking, "What did you take? What did you take?"

The next thing I was aware of I was in a hospital bed and a nurse was standing over me, talking to me. "Celeste, you really gave us a scare," she said, "but I don't want you to worry about anything. We're going to help you."

"Oh, my God!" I cried. "Why didn't you let me die?"

"You came close," she said. "Now try not to think."

I didn't know it was possible to feel this weak and exhausted. I began to cry helplessly. I had absolutely no self control. I didn't have the strength to pick up my head. It was as though my body was dead and only my mind was alive.

The nurse was smoothing my hair back from my face. "I'm going to give you an intravenous," she said.

I didn't even feel the needle go in.

"The doctor wants you to start taking fluids," she said, holding a bent straw to my mouth.

I shook my head no. One way or another I would find a way to end my life. So far all I had succeeded in doing was making things a hundred times worse, taking all those Seconols. I kept drifting in and out of sleep.

In the evening I glanced around and saw that I was in a ward. I closed my eyes and went back to sleep. When I next awoke sunlight was streaming through the windows. Nurses aides kept pestering me with trays of food and glasses of gingerale. I kept refusing the food and was given another intravenous feeding.

The next thing I knew Rita was talking to me. "Mother and I are here," she said.

I looked at Mother and her large dark eyes were sunken into deep charcoal circles. "Baby, don't you know we love you?"

Tears began to roll down her cheeks. "Celeste, what has happened to you that you could do such a thing? You used to be such a good girl, so close to the Lord, always going to church."

"Mother, don't worry about me," I said. "I'll be all right." But I was so weak and depressed, I couldn't keep back the tears.

"The doctor says you'll feel better sooner if you'll start eating," Rita said. "And Rosenthal drove your car to the hospital. He left the keys with the office downstairs."

The tears kept rolling down my cheeks. I had no will to stop them. "Melanie wanted to visit you," Rita said, "but the nurse would allow only Mother and me in."

I closed my eyes. I didn't want to talk to them. I didn't want to listen to them. As I fell back to sleep, Mother was holding my hand.

The next day I felt a little better and began sipping the gingerale an aide kept putting on my nighttable. Later that morning a doctor came over to my bedside. "I'm Dr. Hudson, the resident psychiatrist," he said. "How do you feel?"

"Awful," I said.

"I'd like to help you if you'll let me," he said kindly.

"No one can help me," I said.

"Celeste, the staff is familiar with your problems. We know about the indictments, but you can be helped. Would you answer a few questions?"

"All right," I said. It was easier than arguing.

"When you were growing up, did your mother love your father?"

"What?" Then before he could ask anything else, I said, "Of course, she did."

"Tell me a little about your father. What were your feelings toward him as a child?"

The last thing I wanted to think about was my family so in as few words as possible I tried to answer him. "My father was an alcoholic all his life," I said, keeping my voice flat. "He beat my mother regularly for as long as I can remember. And if any of us kids got in the way, he punched us. Sometimes he beat us too, especially me because I was the smallest and couldn't run away like the others."

"How do you feel about your father now?"

"I love him, I guess," I said, my voice cracking.

He asked more questions but I was too depressed to talk anymore.

"You're tired," he said. "Rest now and I'll see you tomorrow."

I closed my eyes. Later I heard a woman saying, "Miss Clemente, I'd like to speak to you."

I opened my eyes and a middle-aged woman was standing at the foot of the bed. "I'm Mrs. Newberry," she said, smiling. "I'm a social worker and I'd like to help you."

What was the matter with these people? Did they really think they could help me?

She rolled my bed up so that I was in a sitting position. "Dear, the thing for you to think about is learning a vocation. Arrangements can be made for you to go to a trade school."

Against my will I began crying. All I'd done since I got into this hospital was cry.

"Are you able to pay your hospital bill?" she asked.

"I'm broke," I said. "My lawyer took all my money."

"Don't you worry about it," she said. "Welfare will pay your bill. I'll make the necessary arrangements."

She rolled my bed down and left.

Later when an aide walked by I said, "Would you please pull the curtain around my bed so I can have some privacy?"

"We're not permitted to do that," she said. "In this ward the patients have to be watched."

I closed my eyes and silently screamed. "Oh, God, why didn't you let me die?" If only all these people would leave me alone. If only I had the strength, I would get up and jump out a window. Finally I fell asleep.

An aide woke me up for lunch. "I don't want anything to eat," I said.

"Then you'll just keep getting intravenous feedings," she said and left.

Later a man walked over and stood at the foot of my bed. He was a priest. "Miss Clemente, I'm Father Buchanan," he said. "May I speak to you for a few minutes?"

"Yes, Father," I said.

He looked at me with compassion. "I know about your case," he said, "about the indictments. But I'm here to ask if you know that God loves you."

"It may be hard to believe, Father, but when I was a kid I loved the Lord. I used to go to church all the time until I was fifteen. When I got into prostitution I thought it would be only temporary until I met my Prince Charming. But it was like waiting for a horse that never came in."

"I can understand that," he said. "But do you understand that God will forgive you?"

"Yes, Father," I said.

"I'll be praying for you," he said and left.

It was true God loved me. It was true God would forgive me. But it was too late. God couldn't keep me out of prison. God couldn't ease my family's grief and shame. Long, wracking sobs shook my body and I cried, "Oh, God, why don't You just save me and take me?"

At that moment I heard a sound at the end of the ward and I looked toward the doorway. Two black women had just come in. They walked with authority and I felt a strange presence in the room. Both women were smiling and I noticed each one was carrying a Bible. At the sight of the Bible my mind flashed back to the time I was a little girl in church with my arms raised, saying, "Lord, I'll serve you all the days of my life!" I remembered the people who were baptized with the Holy Ghost, slain under the power of God and speaking in other tongues. Suddenly a thought interrupted me: God is not real, God is dead.

"The baptism of the Holy Ghost is real!" I cried. I called out to the two women and when they reached my bedside I said, "Please pray for me. When I was a child I knew Jesus, but I've been a prostitute..."

Their faces took on that joyful look I'd seen so often on Grandma's face. "Praise the Lord!" they both cried.

"I saw your picture in the paper," one woman said. "You're Celeste Clemente!"

I nodded. With that both of them laid their hands upon my head and began praising God. Then they started praying in tongues. One woman cried out in a loud voice, "Father, this is your child! Jesus died on the cross for her sins, just as He died for Mary Magdalene!"

I raised my arms and the woman's voice thundered, "Satan, I command you in the name of Jesus Christ to come out of this girl!"

In a sudden convulsive movement, I felt something leave my body and I knew it was a Satanic spirit. Then the most glorious feeling flooded my being! Jesus rushed into my heart in a wave of love and tears of joy coursed down my cheeks.

The women were weeping and praising God. Then one of them began to read from the Bible about Mary Magdalene. " 'Go and tell my disciples that I have risen,' Jesus commanded her."

I could just hear the feet of Mary Magdalene running through the streets of Jerusalem. I could hear her voice ringing out, "My God is not dead! He's alive!"

I jumped out of that bed and ran to the window. I pushed it open and for the first time I saw that the sky was blue, the grass was green and birds were singing! I thought of the D. A. and I didn't hate him. I didn't even hate the judge. I thought of Ray and I was no longer heartbroken. I had found my Prince Charming and He would never leave me nor forsake me. I remembered my grieving family and not even that could rob me of my new found joy! I was facing life in prison and I didn't care! Jesus Christ had sentenced me to eternal life with Him in heaven. And my heaven had already begun right here on earth because I was born again!

Chapter XXI

"...Behold, All Things Are Become New"

I went to the nurse's station.

"Celeste, what are you doing out of bed? What happened to you?" the nurse asked.

"I never felt better in my life," I said. "I'm going home to see my family."

"A half hour ago you could hardly hold your head up!"

"Would you please send for my things, including my car keys?"

"You can't leave just like that," she said. "There are regulations. The doctor will want to see you."

"I'm signing out," I said.

"Well, you certainly look like a different girl!" she said. "If you want to leave, I can't stop you."

Within minutes I had my clothes on. I walked out of that hospital, got in my Cadillac and drove out of the city limits. As I drove over the parkways to Long Island I kept praising the Lord. I'd never been so happy in all my life. I couldn't wait to tell Mother and Grandma. They would be overjoyed! Then I thought of Melanie. I would bring Melanie to Jesus and she would be saved. With Jesus she wouldn't even be concerned about having to kick her habit. I could hardly wait to tell her.

When I arrived in front of my house, I got out of the car and ran up the steps and started pounding on the door. Mother opened the door and her eyes widened and then a look of joy crossed her face.

"Mother, oh, Mother!" I cried. "I've come back to Jesus!"

"Oh, Celeste! You didn't have to tell me," she said. "The moment I saw you, I saw Jesus in your face!"

She put her arms around me and we stood there, weeping and rejoicing. I finally broke away from her and as I walked into the living room, I saw Dad sitting in his chair in the corner. Instead of freezing, I went over to him and put my arms around him. "Dad, it doesn't matter about the case anymore," I said. "I've come back to Jesus!"

For the first time since the arrest he looked into my eyes. "That's gooda!" he said.

Mother was on the phone telling Grandma to come over. When she came in, I rushed up to her. "Grandma, your prayers have been answered!" I cried. "I've come back to Jesus!"

"Oh, praise the Lord!" she cried. "I always knew He would bring you back. I was determined to pray you through. Oh, Celeste, I'm so happy for you!"

The tears were streaming down her face and she raised her arms and began praising God. I'd never seen Grandma so joyful. She was dancing in the Spirit and praising God at the top of her voice.

"Celeste, your old Sunday school teacher, Mary Richards, called today," Mother said. "Since the raid she has called regularly and her prayer group has been praying for you every day. Please call her."

"Oh, wait 'till Mary Richards hears about this!" I said.

"Mary has been praying for you, Celeste, since you left the Pentecostal church eleven years ago," Grandma said.

I called the Richards and Mary told me to come right over.

When I entered their home, Mary and Ed greeted me. "I was saved today!" I told them. They both put their arms around me and we stood there, praising God.

The telephone rang and Mary answered it. "It's David Wilkerson for you, Ed," she said.

Mary then told me that David Wilkerson was the director of Teen Challenge, a residence for young people who had been into crime and drugs, but who were now born again Christians.

"It's a highly successful program," she said. "The young people are carefully supervised and taught the Word of God."

It sounded like the perfect place for Melanie.

Mary then took the phone from Ed and I heard her telling David Wilkerson a little about me. She put the receiver down for a moment. "Celeste, David wants to know if you can go to Brooklyn tomorrow. He'd like to see you at 1 p.m."

"I'd like to meet him," I said. "Ask him if I can bring a friend."

When I was back home I called Melanie every half hour at the hotel until I reached her at 7 p.m.

"Celeste, how are you? I've been so worried about you!"

"Melanie, you never have to worry about me again," I said. "I've never been happier."

"Did you take something?"

I laughed, "No. I'll tell you all about it tomorrow. I'll pick you up at noon."

"Good, I can't wait to see you!"

"We're going to Teen Challenge," I said.

"Never heard of it," she said. "But I don't care where we go."

The following day when I stopped in front of the hotel to pick up Melanie, for the first time I was struck by the expression in her eyes. In the past I had seen only her flawless beauty. Now I saw the despair in her eyes.

As soon as she was in the car I said, "Melanie, I can't tell you the joy I have found! Honey, I have been born again by the Spirit of God!"

"Have you gone on an acid trip or something?"

"Melanie, Jesus is the answer!"

"What are you talking about?"

"When Jesus died on the cross, He took the punishment for our sins. He saved us from hell."

"I'm not worried about going to hell," she said. "It's the hell on earth I'm worried about."

"Melanie, you don't have to have hell on earth anymore. Once you're born again, Jesus lives in you and no matter what your problems are, nothing can really bother you again!"

"Have you lost your mind?"

"I'm the living proof of what Jesus can do," I said. "I'm facing a life sentence and I don't care!"

"I'm happy for you, Celeste, but I don't want that kind of religion."

"It's not religion," I said. "It's having Jesus in your heart forever!"

I couldn't make her understand, but I was sure David Wilkerson would be able to. About forty minutes later we were sitting in his office. "Celeste, your old Sunday school teacher tells me that Jesus has performed a miracle in your life!" he said.

"The greatest miracle you ever heard of!" I said. "I was a prostitute for two years."

"The greater the forgiveness, the greater the love for Jesus," he said. Then looking at Melanie, David asked, "And what about you, Melanie? Are you saved?"

"I'm not sure what that means," she said.

"Do you know Jesus Christ as your personal Savior?"

"Of course," she said. "Anyone, who believes in Jesus knows He is the Savior."

"But have you had a personal experience with Jesus in your heart that has totally changed you?" he asked.

"I don't think it's possible to be significantly changed,"

she said.

"It is possible to be completely changed in an instant, but only through the power of God," David said. "Melanie, to be saved, first you have to acknowledge Jesus as your Savior. Second, you have to repent of all the sins of your life. Then ask Him to come into your heart and be Lord of your life."

"I've done that many times," she said.

"You can be born again only once," David said. "We were all born spiritually blinded by Satan. Until we are born again, Satan is our spiritual father and we are living for him. The only way you can have your spiritual eyes opened is miraculously by Jesus Christ. Only then do you stop living for Satan and start living for God. That is being born again."

"I was brought up a Catholic," she said, "and I don't go for all that jazz." Melanie stood up. "I'll wait for you in the lobby, Celeste," she said and left.

"Don't worry about Melanie," David said. "You can't bring her into the family of God unless the Holy Spirit has been drawing her."

"But David, she's my best friend!"

"Put her in the hands of God," he said. "Now, as for you, Celeste, I would like you to move into Teen Challenge. You need to grow in the Lord. You have to be spiritually fed because you're just a babe in Christ. Right now you need personal guidance. If you remain in the world, you will probably backslide."

I readily agreed to move in. I knew this was where God wanted me. I said goodbye to David and with a heavy heart I walked to the lobby. Melanie was pacing the floor. "Melanie, I'm staying at Teen Challenge," I said. "This is the place for me."

"Well, it's not the place for me," she said.

I never felt so frustrated. Couldn't she see the miraculous change in me? Didn't she want the peace I had?

"Melanie, I love you and want you to have the joy and peace of the Lord," I said. "I want to know before I go to prison that you are destined for heaven and delivered from drugs."

"Celeste, this is hard for me to say because you've been my best friend, but I just can't buy that Jesus bit. I'm never going to give up drugs, except while I'm in prison. And I'm not worried about salvation."

I walked with her to the door.

She kissed me on the cheek. "Thanks for everything," she said.

I kissed her good bye and stood in the doorway and watched as she walked down the street. Then I began to cry. I couldn't understand it. Melanie had taken my advice on everything, but when it came to the most important thing in her life, Jesus, she had turned her back.

That night when I went to bed at Teen Challenge, I made a vow. "I was a dynamite sinner," I said. "and now, Jesus, I vow that I'm going to be dynamite for you!"

The following day a counselor was assigned to me. Agnes was twenty-nine years old and she'd been in Teen Challenge for eight months. "I found Jesus when I was turning tricks for $5," she said. "Things were really bad. I had a heavy drug habit to support and I knew I couldn't last much longer. Then one night a young girl stopped me on the street and handed me a tract that explained salvation. I gave my heart to Jesus right there and in that instant I lost all desire for heroin. I moved into Teen Challenge and I've been on a high for Jesus ever since!"

Agnes watched me day and night. I was not allowed to go anywhere alone. The people who ran Teen Challenge were aware of the pitfalls. I adjusted quickly to the new routine. Every morning I was up at 6:30. For the first time in my life I ate a big breakfast. Each morning we went to the chapel for service and listened to David preach. Those sermons put my heart on fire for the Lord. There were counseling sessions if we needed them, and there were Bible studies. As a youngster I had heard the Word of God preached, but I had never read the Bible myself. Now I couldn't get enough of the scriptures. When I put the Bible down in the morning, I couldn't wait to get back to it in the afternoon. Each night after supper we went to the chapel for the evening service.

"When you people leave here," David said one night, "you will be preaching the gospel of Jesus Christ. You will be bringing souls into the kingdom of God!"

That was what I wanted to do more than anything in the world—win souls for Jesus.

At Teen Challenge I found real love, love I could count on. The students and staff loved me, not with human love that was so erratic and limited, but with the love of Jesus.

I never missed the alcohol that had been such a big part of my life for the past six years. I never felt the need for a sleeping pill or an amphetamine. Jesus had really set me free. But through all the joy and freedom, there were times I became depressed. I felt I had committed the worst possible sin and I was plagued with guilt and remorse. Finally I went to see Mrs. Daly, one of the counselors.

As I walked into her office tears came to my eyes. "What's the matter, Celeste?" she asked.

"I know Jesus forgave my sins," I said, "but I can't stop thinking about what I did. I feel such remorse, such guilt, that I can't stand it!"

"I'm not surprised you feel like that," she said. "The devil wants to rob you of your joy. If he can defeat you, then you won't be of much use to the Lord."

I'd never heard of such a thing.

"Remember that when Jesus died on the cross, He not only forgave your sins, He also forgot them."

She wrote something on an index card. "Celeste, keep this on your dresser," she said. "Memorize this scripture and whenever the devil tries to get you down, resist him by quoting this scripture and say, 'Thank you for the blood,

Jesus.' "

I took the card from her and read it. "I, even I, am he that blotteth out thy transgressions for mine own sake, and will not remember thy sins." (Isaiah 43:25)

I'd been in Teen Challenge a little over three weeks when Melanie had to go to court for sentencing. I was given permission to go to court with my counselor, Agnes.

As Melanie walked into the courtroom with Mr. Coughlin her eyes were wide with fright. When she saw me she just nodded. She'd had her last fix this morning, I knew.

Judge Baylor banged his gavel. "This court will come to order," he said. "The defendant will rise."

Melanie and Mr. Coughlin stood before the bench.

"Miss Morrison, is there anything you care to say before this court passes sentence on you?" the judge asked.

"No, your honor," she said.

"I hereby sentence the defendant, Miss Melanie Morrison, to six months in the Women's House of Detention for the crime of prostitution. Next case."

Melanie stood there unmoving as the guard put handcuffs on her. I went up to her.

"Melanie, this could be a blessing in disguise," I said. "There's no other way you're going to kick your habit. When you get out, you can make a decent life for yourself."

"Oh, Celeste, I'm so afraid!" she said.

"I'll be praying for you," I said.

The guard took her out to the paddy wagon and I left.

A week later David Wilkerson summoned me to his office. His desk was covered with newspaper clippings that I immediately recognized from the raid.

"Celeste, is this you?" he asked, pointing to the clippings.

"Yes," I said. "I was going to tell you all about my case eventually."

"Well, I've heard of Rahab and Mary Magdalene," he said. "I've preached about them. But I just don't know if someone with your fame and fortune could stay in a place like

Teen Challenge. This is a humble little place."

"David, money used to be my god. I had all the money anyone could want, but it was ashes. Since I found Jesus, I don't care about material things. In Jesus I have love, joy, and peace of mind!"

"You know what?" He grinned. "I think you're going to make it."

The longer I was saved the more unbelievable my former life seemed. By immersing myself in the scriptures, I became closer to Jesus. I spent more time in prayer and couldn't get enough of the Lord. Now I could understand how Grandma had been able to have peace and joy during all the years Grandpa beat her. Now nothing could come between Jesus and me.

Three months after I'd moved into Teen Challenge David said to me, "Celeste, you are progressing so rapidly in the Lord that I think you're ready for a Kathryn Kuhlman meeting."

I'd never heard of Miss Kuhlman. "I'll go anywhere for Jesus," I said.

"Would you be willing to give your testimony to thirty thousand people?"

"Of course," I said.

A few nights later I was in Pittsburgh having dinner with David. "Celeste, I want to put your mind at ease," he said. "Miss Kuhlman and I have discussed this and because you're still a babe in Christ, I'll tell part of your background tonight and then you'll answer questions."

One hour later I entered the Soldiers and Sailors Memorial Building and I was immediately escorted onto the stage. I took a seat with the group of people on stage. David was speaking through the microphone telling the audience about me and after a few minutes he motioned me to join him. "I want you to meet Celeste, a modern day Mary Magdalene," he said.

I looked out at the sea of faces and everyone was clapping.

David handed me a microphone and said, "Celeste, tell us when you got started in prostitution."

"It was over two years ago, when I was twenty-four," I said.

"And what happened?"

"At first I thought it would be temporary," I said, "but I was making so much money, I couldn't stop. Then I began drinking heavily. Next I was popping pills. I became the madam of the largest prostitution ring in New York."

There were gasps all over the auditorium.

"Did you ever think you would get out of that life?" David asked.

"Yes, I always thought I would meet Prince Charming and he would sweep me off my feet and we would live happily ever after."

"But what happened?"

"I was arrested last February," I said. "I was indicted on twenty-seven felonies and ten misdemeanors. I'm facing life imprisonment."

I heard women crying. Others were calling on the name of the Lord.

"How did you react to that?" David asked.

"I tried to commit suicide," I said, "but the doctors were able to revive me."

People were crying openly now.

"Later two missionaries came into the hospital ward and prayed for me," I said as tears started coursing down my cheeks. "They cast out a demonic spirit and Jesus came into my heart. Jesus has given me a new heart and a new life..." My voice broke and I couldn't say another word.

Everyone in the auditorium was standing and the applause was deafening. Voices were raised, praising God and I could feel the love of Jesus all over me.

"Here you see the transforming power of Jesus Christ!" David said.

Kathryn Kuhlman came over to me and took my hand.

"Celeste, this is your day, darling!" she said. Then putting her arms around me she prayed. "Jesus, this is what you went to the cross for!" Her voice rose as she quoted scripture. "But God hath chosen the foolish things of the world to confound the wise, and God hath chosen the weak things to confound the things which are mighty, and the base things which are despised, hath God chosen...That no flesh should glory in his presence." (I Corinthians 1:27-29)

Chapter XXII

The Trial

My trial date on the charge of prostitution was scheduled for the following week. I had to smile when I recalled how bitter and angry I'd been at previous court appearances. Now, instead of dreading it, I had complete peace of mind. From the moment I'd been born again, Jesus had erased all hate and hostility from my heart.

It was a hot day in July when Agnes and I went to Rosenthal's office. As soon as he saw me he said, "Celeste, what happened to you? I hardly recognize you!"

"I have found Jesus Christ as my personal Savior," I said. "And He has given me a new heart."

Rosenthal studied me for a long moment, then shook his head. "Well, I'm glad you're happy because, as you know, this trial is going to end in a conviction."

"It doesn't bother me now," I said.

Picking up a folder he said, "Well, let's go over a few things. You'll be convicted on the charge of prostitution. That is a misdemeanor, punishable by a six-month term usually. You'll get time off for good behavior. In any event, this is nothing compared to the next trial. At the next trial you will be tried for procuring, maintaining a disorderly house, and living off the proceeds of prostitutes. These are felonies. That's the trial to worry about."

"Mr. Rosenthal, you don't seem to understand. I'm not worried about either trial."

He looked at me in disbelief. "It's beyond me," he said. Then he told me what I could expect at the trial, what Andy and Ray might say on the stand and he schooled me in my responses.

"I'll just tell the truth," I said.

"At this point it would be foolish not to," he said.

We drove to 100 Center Street, New York City and when we entered the courthouse the photographers and reporters were waiting in the hallway. We walked past them and at nine thirty we were inside the courtroom. Rita came in as Rosenthal and I sat down at the witness table. Mr. O'Rourke was walking in with Andy and Ray. I watched Ray as he walked to the other witness table and I felt nothing but compassion for him. He kept looking down so that our eyes wouldn't meet. When I recalled the devastation and heartache over him, I could hardly believe that I felt no bitterness, no sorrow. Ray's face was drawn into tight, hard lines and he stared straight ahead. Andy glanced in my direction, then quickly looked away.

After the preliminaries were over with, Judge Baylor said, "The defendant will please stand."

Rosenthal and I stood before the judge.

"Is the defendant, Celeste Clemente, here?" the judge asked impatiently.

"Your honor," I said, "I am standing before you."

He looked at me momentarily, then said to Rosenthal, "Where is the defendant?"

"She's right here, your honor," Rosenthal said, pointing to me.

"That's not the same woman I saw in this courtroom last February," Judge Baylor said.

"Your honor," I said, "I am Celeste Clemente."

"Young lady, I must warn you that impersonating another person is a crime."

Voices were raised in the back of the courtroom.

"Your honor, I am the accused madam," I said.

"Bring in the policewoman who was in the raid," the judge said to the court clerk.

The policewoman came into the courtroom and stood before the bench.

"Are you the same officer who searched the defendant, Celeste Clemente, during the raid on February 14?" the judge asked.

"I am, your honor," she said.

"Can you identify this young woman as the accused madam?" he asked.

The policewoman studied me for a moment. "It looks like her," she said, "but I can't swear it is the same woman."

I had to smile. When the Lord saved me He changed the way I walked, the way I talked. He had changed my entire countenance.

Judge Baylor called the clerk over. "Bring in two plainclothes men who assisted in the raid," he said.

When the detectives came in I recognized them. The night of the raid the Irish-looking one had put on a blonde wig and danced around my bedroom. The other one had stood guard over Lana.

"Detective Maloney, can you identify this woman as the accused madam?" Judge Baylor asked.

The cop looked at me carefully. "Your honor, she looks like the woman we arrested in the raid," he said, "but I cannot make a positive identification."

I could hear Rita laughing softly.

Judge Baylor banged his gavel. "Order in the courtroom!" The second detective made the same response.

"Your honor," I said, "why don't you take my fingerprints? Fingerprints don't lie."

The judge looked from Rosenthal to O'Rourke. Then looking at me he said, "That's a good idea."

I was taken downstairs by the guard and fingerprinted.

Forty-five minutes later the report on my prints was ready and the guard handed it to the judge and said, "Your honor, this is the woman!"

"Amazing!" the judge said. "It certainly doesn't look like her."

Finally the trial got underway.

Mr. O'Rourke said, "I call Detective Andrew Forrester to the stand."

Andy took the oath and sat down. "Would you tell the court, Detective Forrester, where you work?" O'Rourke asked.

"I work as a plainclothes detective in the district attorney's office in Queens County," Andy said. "I'm in the Vice Squad."

"Please tell the court what happened on the night of February 14," O'Rourke said.

"On February 14, I went with Detective Donahue to Celeste's apartment at 8 p.m. Detective Donahue introduced me to Celeste. Then she and I went into a bedroom for the purpose of prostitution. I asked her how much it would be and she said one hundred dollars. I gave her ten ten-dollar bills in marked money," he said.

I knew everyone in the courtroom believed him.

"Then what happened?" O'Rourke asked.

"I pulled out my badge, identified myself as a police officer, and arrested her," Andy said.

"You may step down," O'Rourke said.

"I call Detective Donahue to the stand," O'Rourke said.

Ray went up to the witness stand and put his hand on the Bible.

"Do you swear to tell the truth, the whole truth, and nothing but the truth?" the clerk asked.

"I do," Ray said. He sat down and looked at O'Rourke. His face was flushed and I could feel only pity for him.

"Would you tell the court, Detective Donahue, where you work?" O'Rourke asked.

"I'm a plainclothes detective in the District Attorney's office," he said. "I work in the Robbery Squad."

"Please tell the court what happened on the night of February 14," O'Rourke said.

"On the night of February 14, I took Detective Forrester to Miss Clemente's apartment at eight o'clock. It was a prearranged meeting and she was expecting us." The muscle in his right cheek was twitching.

"Go on, please," O'Rourke said.

"When we arrived I introduced Miss Clemente to Andy, to Detective Forrester, and they went into a bedroom." Ray kept his eyes riveted on O'Rourke. "Detective Forrester put her under arrest for prostitution."

"Then what happened, Detective Donahue?" O'Rourke asked.

"I called the D. A.'s office and I remained in Miss Clemente's apartment until the raid got under way a few minutes later."

"You may step down," O'Rourke said.

People in the back of the courtroom were whispering.

Judge Baylor banged his gavel. "This court will come to order!" he said.

Rosenthal stood before the bench and said, "I call Miss Clemente to the stand."

I walked up to the witness stand and took the oath.

"You may be seated," the clerk said.

I gave my name and address and Rosenthal said, "Please tell the court what happened on the night of February 14."

"Detective Donahue and Detective Forrester came to my apartment at eight o'clock," I said. "Detective Forrester and I went into a bedroom for the purpose of prostitution. When he asked me how much it would cost, I said, 'It's on the house. You're a friend of Ray's.' "

There was a sudden commotion in the courtroom and the judge banged his gavel.

"This court will not tolerate any more disturbances!"

"Are you saying no money passed between you and Detective Forrester?" Rosenthal asked.

"Yes, that's what I'm saying."

"Miss Clemente, will you tell the court what your relationship was with Detective Donahue?" Rosenthal asked.

"I was in love with Detective Donahue," I said. "He never caught me in the act of prostitution on the night of February 14 or at any other time. And at no time did any money pass between us."

I glanced at the judge. His head was thrown back and his eyes were closed. He obviously thought I was lying.

"You may step down," Rosenthal said.

I walked back to the witness table and glanced quickly at Ray. His face was a dark red and he was frowning.

"Looking at this case we find that the defendant, Miss Celeste Clemente, was convicted on the same charge one year ago," Judge Baylor said. "Based on ascertained information this court finds the defendant guilty of prostitution. Sentencing to be on August 15 at 9:30. Bail continued. Next case."

Rosenthal and I rushed out of the courtroom with the reporters shouting questions behind us. Rita, realizing I was trying to evade the press, just waved. As we waited for the elevator the reporters converged upon us. "Celeste, now that you heard Donahue testify against you and you've been convicted, how do you feel about him?" a reporter asked.

"If Ray Donahue were blind," I said, "I would give him my eyes."

Chapter XXIII

The Rathole

Since Jesus had come into my heart, life was one miracle after the other. Not even the prospect of going to prison could rob me of the peace of God. One month later I was in the courtroom standing before Judge Baylor again. "Is there anything you'd like to say on your own behalf before this court passes sentence on you?" the judge asked.

"Yes, your honor," I said. "I would like to say that I did not take any money that was offered to me by Detective Forrester. He and Detective Donahue were both lying."

"I hereby sentence the defendant, Celeste Clemente, to a six-month term in the Women's House of Detention," he said.

Rita rushed up to me, crying.

"It's all right, Rita," I said. "Jesus is with me."

Mr. Rosenthal shook my hand. "I'll be in touch with you," he said and left.

I paid no attention to the reporters as the guard put handcuffs on my wrists. I walked out to the paddy wagon and was driven to the Women's House of Detention. I hoped I would be put in the same section with Melanie. She would be there almost another two weeks.

When I was inside the prison I was stripped of my jewelry and clothing and given prison clothes. I put on the pink cotton uniform and the black socks and black oxford shoes. They were the ugliest shoes I had ever seen. Then I was escorted by a female guard through a corridor. She kept eyeing me and I could feel her resentment. We stopped in front of a cell. "This is your new home," she said, "and remember, you might have been high and mighty on the outside, but in this place you're less than nothing, Madam!"

"Welcome to the Rathole!" the young woman in my cell said. "I'm Sandy. I saw your picture in the newspaper. Wow! You sure made a hot story for the D. A. The whole jail is talking about all the money you made!"

I laughed. "Glad to meet you, Sandy," I said. Right away I knew we'd be friends.

"I just got here myself a couple of hours ago," she said. I noticed that she was sweating.

"This place is loaded with Black Panthers," she said. "You've got to watch out. I hear they cut you up if you look at them wrong."

"I'm not worried about anything," I said.

I looked around and saw that all I had besides a cot was a towel and a bar of soap. A few minutes later when a guard walked by I asked if I could have a Bible. "I'll get one for you from the library," she said.

"I got busted for vagrancy," Sandy said. "I'm only in for thirty days, but I'm not going to make it."

"Why? What's wrong?" I asked.

"I've been into heroin for three years and when you kick cold turkey like this, I hear you can die within twenty-four hours."

"Sandy, you don't have a thing to worry about!" I said. "Jesus will set you free. He performed a miracle in my life and He'll do the same for you!"

Her eyes widened. I told her about my conversion and explained the plan of salvation. Tears welled in her eyes and she said, "Celeste, last night I prayed for the first time in many years. I wasn't even sure there was a God, but now I know He's real. I can see Him in you."

Sandy repeated the sinner's prayer after me: "Jesus, I acknowledge You as my Savior and I repent of all the sins of my life. I ask you to come into my heart, Jesus, and become Lord of my life!"

Tears were sliding down her cheeks and I cried out, "Oh, thank you, Jesus!"

These words were greeted with wild laughter from the cell to our right.

"My, oh my! What have we got here?" Cora, a young Black Panther called out. "A holy roller! Just what this joint needs!"

Sandy and I were so happy and joyful, it didn't matter what anyone said.

A little later I heard a voice from the other end of the corridor shout, "Come and get your dog food!"

A guard was walking through the corridor, unlocking gates. We had to walk two by two through the corridors until we reached the mess hall. The meal consisted of ox-tails, overcooked beans, watery canned corn and lukewarm, weak coffee. Sandy could not eat anything. I could hardly get the food down myself and as I ate I saw three cockroaches crawling up the leg of our table.

"Hey aren't you the Big Madam?" a fat, middle-aged inmate at our table asked me. "Sure. I seen your picture in every paper in town. You don't look so big now!" She laughed convulsively.

Immediately there was a commotion at our table and the woman repeated the lurid news accounts of the raid to the other women. They were all obviously familiar with my case. Everyone at the table was staring at me.

"She made two hundred and fifty grand a year!" a young woman across from me said.

"Where's all the dough now, Madam?" another one asked.

Most of them started laughing and I just looked at my plate.

When we got back to our cell, Sandy was holding her abdomen. "I have such cramps," she cried. "I can't stand it."

Later she was sick to her stomach. When she was lying on her cot, I soaked my towel in cold water, wrung it out and held it against her forehead. I stroked her hair away from her face and kept praying. By late afternoon Sandy was shaking. "I've got to have a fix!" she cried. "I'll lose my mind if I don't have a fix!"

When it was time for supper I didn't want to leave Sandy, but the guard said I would get in trouble if I didn't go to the mess hall.

"Can't someone help Sandy?" I asked. "Couldn't she be seen by a doctor?"

The guard laughed shortly. "Do you know how many junkies we get in this joint? We'd have to have a doctor on call twenty-four hours a day just for them! It's her own fault. No doctor can help her now!" she said.

After supper Sandy was worse. I dreaded what would happen next. I remembered Melanie screaming when she'd tried to kick her habit.

At seven o'clock the inmates filed into the corridor to go to the Rec Room. When I remained in my cell, the guard came over to me. "Why aren't you going to the Rec Room like everyone else?" she asked.

"I want to stay with my cellie," I said. "She's a very sick girl."

"You're crazy, girl! You can't help her!" The guard left.

Late that night Sandy was doubled over with cramps. When she didn't have diarrhea, she was throwing up. She began crying helplessly. I had prayed all day that Jesus would deliver her and now I got up and put both my hands on her head and cried out in a loud voice, "Jesus, right now set Sandy free!"

Sandy's grip on the bars loosened and her body relaxed.

She turned to me and said, "Celeste, it's a miracle! No more pain! I'm fine!"

"Oh, thank you, Jesus!" I cried.

Tears of joy were streaming down Sandy's face and the two of us rejoiced. I was profoundly humbled. I had prayed for a miracle and Jesus had performed it! I was overwhelmed with love for Him. As Sandy and I stood there praising God, Cora cried out, "Oh, God, forgive me! I want what those girls have!"

I walked over to the right and prayed with Cora. She gave her heart to Jesus and now the three of us raised our voices, praising God.

Word of Sandy's miracle spread fast and the next morning some of the inmates were no longer laughing at me.

After breakfast a pleasant looking guard came up to me and said, "I'm Mrs. Jones. Some of the girls call me Mother Jones. I'm supposed to take you down to meet the warden."

I smiled at her and as we walked through the halls, Mother Jones said, "Honey, if there's ever anything I can do for you, don't hesitate to ask."

"Thank you, Mother Jones!" I said.

When we got off the elevator on the first floor there were two guards in the hallway. They stared at me. "Well, here comes the Big Madam!" one of them said. They both laughed.

When we were out of earshot Mother Jones said, "Honey, you're going to have to put up with a lot around here."

"It's okay," I said. "I can take it."

Mother Jones took me into an office and introduced me to the warden, Mrs. Flagstaff, a big black woman. The warden looked me over carefully. "Celeste, I don't want any trouble from you," she said.

"Yes, Maam," I said.

"If I get any flak from you, I will personally see to it that you will not make any good time."

"Yes, Maam," I said.

We left her office and Mother Jones took me into the Rehabilitation Office and introduced me to the supervisor, Mrs. Hahn. Mrs. Hahn glared at me. "You'll be working in here as a typist," she said. "Two hours in the morning and two hours in the afternoon." Then leaning across her desk she added, "All them big bucks you got stashed away won't do you no good in here. You'll be treated like anyone else."

Mother Jones said goodbye and I began my first day's work for Mrs. Hahn. She put a report on my desk and told me to type it. Then bringing her face close to mine she said, "Just because we're black, don't mean we're maids!"

For the remainder of the morning she continued to bait me, but I never responded.

After supper that night I went to the Rec Room with Sandy. I had to find Melanie. As soon as I walked in I spotted her. She was playing ping pong. I walked over to the table and stood quietly, waiting for her to notice me. Her thick dark hair shone and her eyes sparkled. Even though she was wearing that cheap cotton uniform and those awful black oxfords, Melanie never looked more beautiful. I laughed suddenly and she turned her head in my direction. "Celeste!" she cried and dropped her paddle and ran to me. She hugged me. "Am I glad to see you!" she said.

"Melanie, you never looked better," I said.

"I'll be out in eleven days," she said.

"I'm so happy for you," I said. "You kicked your habit and now you can make a decent life for yourself."

"Yes," she said. "I'm going to enroll in a secretarial school next month."

"Will you give your heart to Jesus?" I asked quietly.

"Oh, Celeste, are you still into that?"

"Once you ask Jesus into your heart, it's forever," I said. "It's not some kind of trip."

She shook her head and I said nothing further. The Holy Spirit would have to lead her.

That night when the lights were turned off in the cells I sat on the edge of my cot, praying for a long time. Everyone was sleeping when I heard a quick, light running sound in my cell. I looked down and there on the floor only inches away from my feet was a huge rat. I pulled my feet up and got under the blanket. Now I knew why this jail had been named the Rathole. Off and on through the night I heard the scurrying sound of a rat running down the corridor.

The next afternoon after we finished our work shift, Cora, Sandy and I held our first Bible study. As I read the scriptures aloud, Emma and Jessica in the cell on my left kept laughing and mocking us. "Madam turned preacher!" Jessica yelled.

"How come she wasn't preachin' before she got in here?" Emma shouted.

Before we went to the mess hall for supper, Sandy spoke to Jessica and Emma. "You dames can laugh all you want," she said, "but this time yesterday I was very sick and last night when I thought I'd go out of my head, Jesus Christ performed a miracle in my life!"

Emma roared laughing. "Honey, we know that was nothing but an act!"

In the mess hall when Sandy saw the food on her tray she said, "What is this supposed to be?"

"It's better if you don't know," I said.

"If I don't look at it, maybe I can eat it," she said.

Not as many women were laughing and staring at me as on the first night. Some of them were touched by Sandy's miracle and one girl, Jenny, came up to us after supper. "I'd like to come to your cell when you have another Bible study," she said.

"Every afternoon between four and five, we'll hold a Bible study," I said. "Everyone is welcome, Jenny."

When it was time to go to the Rec Room, I sat down on my cot and opened my Bible.

"Aren't you going?" Sandy asked.

"No, Sandy," I said. "This is my opportunity to be alone with the Lord."

I was the only inmate left on the tier. I asked the guard to lock me in my cell and she looked at me strangely. "If you'd rather be alone," she said, "that's your problem."

I prayed for my mother and everyone in my family. I had no fear or worry about them anymore. Jesus had given me complete peace about them. I opened the Bible and began reading about Mary Magdalene. Then I prayed and said, "Jesus, after your resurrection, why did you appear to a low prostitute instead of one of the holy women?"

An inaudible but unmistakable voice answered me. "Celeste, it was done to show the grace of God!"

I never felt so close to the Lord. I began to worship and praise Him and soon I forgot where I was. I'd never known such joy and happiness. And as the days passed, this time alone with Jesus each night became the most precious time of my life.

One afternoon I received a kite from Emma. It read: "Dear Celeste, I've been watching you since you came in here. I think you are my kind of woman. I would like to meet you in the Rec Room tonight and discuss our relationship, which I know will grow and blossom into something beautiful. Emma."

When I mentioned the kite to Sandy, I said, "I didn't know Emma was a butch."

"Are you kidding? Ninety percent of the women in here are gay," she said.

I ignored Emma's kite and her meaningful glances. One evening when the inmates were leaving their cells to go to the Rec Room, Emma stood in front of my cell. "Hey, Madam," she said, "what are you, crazy or something? Everyone in this joint is gay!"

"Well, I'm not," I said.

Emma was a very large black woman, over two hundred pounds. She stood there, her eyes blazing. "Just what the hell are you interested in?" she asked.

"God has called me to be a missionary," I said.

She laughed. "What's a missionary doing in jail?" she asked.

She left and I sat down on my cot. For the next two hours I read the scriptures and praised the Lord. I was closer to Him now than I had been at any time before. "Oh, Jesus, I just want to work for you!" I cried. "I just want to bring souls into Your Kingdom!"

One night as I paced back and forth in my cell, praising God, I caught sight of the two guards in the corridor staring at me. They didn't realize I could hear them talking about me. "Why does she want to be locked in there by herself every night?" one asked.

"She's got jail house religion," the other one said.

As the days went by I felt a heavy burden for Emma and Jessica. In spite of their taunts and jeers, I felt I had to witness to them one more time. Looking through the bars at them I said, "Do you know Jesus loves you?"

Emma snorted.

"If you girls will repent of all the sins of your life..."

"Shut up!" Jessica shouted. "Don't you ever talk about that bull shit again!" She brought her face up against the bars. "You be careful, girl, or you'll find a knife in your back!"

I turned away and Sandy came over and whispered, "Celeste, don't say any more to them. These Black Panthers will walk in your blood just for kicks!"

Every Friday when we went to the commissary I was given a chit for $25. And every time, a group of inmates crowded around me, hoping I would pay for their candy or cigarettes. "I'll pay for the candy for those who want to come to the Bible study," I said.

I was aware that many of the inmates were using me, but I also knew that if they heard the Word of God, some of them would be saved. As the weeks went by many inmates gave their hearts to Jesus and there was a marked change in the attitude of others toward me. They now realized that I was not playing church.

On Sundays Mother and Rita came to visit me. I looked forward to their visits, but it was frustrating not to be able to put my arms around Mother. A thick wall of glass separated the visitors from the inmates and I had to stand in a booth and talk to them on a phone. This particular Sunday when I went into the booth I was amazed to see Chris standing with Mother. When he caught my eye, he broke into a big smile. I picked up the phone to speak to him and all I could say was, "Chris..." He had the visitor's phone in his hand and he said, "It's okay, Celeste. Everything is okay." I wished I could hug him. Tears stung my eyes. Tears were in his eyes now and as he stepped aside and let Mother take the phone, I thanked Jesus that Chris had finally forgiven me. I dried my tears and looked at Mother. She was beaming.

"You look better all the time," she said. "I don't understand it."

She could see the joy of the Lord in me. While I was doing time, my family was being reconciled to my past and strengthened by my love for Jesus. And to think not too many months ago I had thought that not even God could rectify my life, that not even God could mend my mother's broken heart or ease my family's shame and grief.

One afternoon when I was alone in my cell Emma walked in. Immediately I was on guard. She took one step toward me, grabbed me by the throat and knocked me down on my cot. "Watch this, Jessie!" she shouted.

She stradled me and I cried out, "The blood of Jesus! The blood of Jesus!"

Her eyes were wild and I could feel the power and force

of her body as she pinned my shoulders to the cot.

"The blood of Jesus!" I screamed again.

Suddenly the fire and strength went out of her and she let go of me and got off the cot. "You're too religious for me," she said and left.

I began pacing back and forth with my arms raised, praising God. I knew no matter what the danger, He would always be there to deliver me.

Two days later Emma was released and the following night Mother Jones stopped by Jessica's cell. "Jessie," she said, "I have bad news about your friend, Emma."

There was a hush throughout the nearby cells as Mother Jones continued. "Emma was killed a few hours ago. She was shot in a holdup."

Jessica broke down sobbing. I thought she was grieving for her friend. Suddenly she called out, "Celeste, can I talk to you?"

"Of course. Come on over, Jessie," I said. I was surprised.

She came into my cell. "Celeste, God has opened my eyes," she said. "I laughed at you just like Emma did, but now I see. I want Jesus!"

I led Jessica in the prayer of salvation and she cried out, "Oh, thank you, Jesus! Thank you, Jesus!" Then taking my hand, she said, "Celeste, God sent you to this rathole just to save people like me!"

After that, my desire to save souls for Jesus was like a fire within me. It seemed I would never be able to tell the good news of salvation to enough people. As a result of Jessica's salvation, two more Black Panthers came to the Bible study and gave their hearts to Jesus. Now the guards who had been harassing me for the first few weeks began to let up. I was no longer greeted as the Big Madam.

I'd been in the Rathole a month when Rita and Mother came with bad news about Grandma. "Grandma had a stroke," Mother said. "Her mind is fine and her spirits are good but the doctor says she won't be able to take care of herself anymore. All of her right side is paralyzed. When she's discharged from the hospital, she's going to be living with Aunt Connie."

"Oh, no!" I cried. I loved Grandma so much I couldn't bear to think of losing her. I would have given anything to see her.

"I cook dinner for Grandpa now and he's doing all right by himself," Mother said.

I recalled what Grandma had once told me. "The Lord has told me that Grandpa will be saved when I die."

When they left I prayed for Grandma and felt the peace of God envelop me. Before being saved, news like this would have torn me apart.

The next day Sandy was released and my new cellie was a young girl named Patti. She was as thin as a rail and I could see she had once been very pretty. "I'm a junkie," she said. "I've been into heroin almost five years."

She started to cry.

"Patti, let me pray for you," I said.

"That won't help," she said. "God never helped me."

Later that day Patti had cramps and diarrhea. By night time she was throwing up and crying. "Oh, God, if you're up there," she cried, "Let me die!"

When the guard walked by our cell I said, "Can't you get a doctor for Patti?"

"I didn't stick the needle in her," the guard said. "Let her drop dead!"

I tried to soothe Patti's tortured body with silent prayer and cold applications to her forehead and face. Patti was worse the next day, sick and moaning continually. The inmates were unusually quiet and some of them were praying for her, I knew. She became weaker and weaker and on the fourth day she went into convulsions, one after another. After that she lay completely motionless on her cot. I took her hand and began talking to her. "Patti, it's Celeste," I

said.

She did not respond. Her face was grey and her eyes were staring vacantly.

"Patti, oh, Patti, say something!" I cried.

She seemed oblivious of her surroundings. I could see a pulse beating faintly in her thin throat.

"Patti, I know you can't talk, but if you want Jesus to come into your heart, blink your eyes, move a finger, do something."

Instantly I felt a slight pressure from her hand.

"Oh, Jesus!" I cried out. "You died on the cross for Patti. She knows you're her Savior and she repents of all the sins of her life. Jesus, Patti wants you to come into her heart right now!"

Again I felt pressure from Patti's hand, this time stronger. I looked down at her and now her eyes were sparkling with joy. Then abruptly her lids closed and the little pulse in her throat stopped beating. I watched her for a long moment, refusing to believe what I saw. Then I cried, "Oh, why did you let her die, Lord?"

Girls all over the tier started crying.

I called to the guard and when she learned what had happened, she disappeared briefly. Within minutes two other guards appeared with a stretcher and took Patti's body away.

For the rest of the night I kept praising God. "Thank you, Jesus, for saving Patti!" I cried over and over. When the lights were turned off and everyone was sleeping, I continued to pray in thanksgiving. Patti had come so close to missing out on salvation. I served a merciful God and I was overwhelmed with gratitude that He would use me to bring souls into His kingdom. In that dark cell I could feel the presence of Jesus and as I prayed, suddenly one side of my cell became illuminated with a brilliant ball of light. "Jesus!" I cried. And as suddenly, the ball of light vanished.

Chapter XXIV

His Missionary

My new cellie was a heavyset black woman, Liza. "I got busted for assaulting a cop!" She laughed.

"What did you do to him?" I asked.

"I kicked him!" she said and roared laughing. "Me and my boyfriend were in this bar and we had too much and got in a fight. Someone called the cops and now I'm here."

I told Liza what I was in for and how the Lord had changed my life.

"Honey, I had an aunt who used to preach that Jesus stuff to me when I was a kid," she said. "I don't need it. When I'm drinking I'm happy. The old juice is all I need."

I told her about the raid and all the court appearances. "My lawyer says the D. A. will delay my case as long as possible, so I don't know when I'll go to trial on the felony charges," I said. "When I went to court in September the D. A. got an adjournment because the witnesses didn't show up. When I went in October, he got another adjournment because he had misfiled some papers. This case could drag on forever. When it does come to trial I'll get five years for each person who testifies against me, so no matter how you look at it, I'll be doing heavy time."

"It's a shame," Liza said, "a beautiful, young girl like

you."

"I'm not concerned," I said. "I have the Lord."

"Oh, here we go again!" She laughed and left the cell.

In the two months I'd been in the Rathole, more and more prisoners were giving their hearts to Jesus. Even though in prison, I'd never been happier in my life because I was doing the Lord's work. But for some reason I couldn't understand why I was becoming very tired as time passed.

My cellie, Liza, was released and a few hours later Terry moved in. She was an attractive young woman in her late twenties. "I got busted for impersonating a policewoman," she said. "It was a good thing while it lasted." She laughed. "I got this young girl to proposition a guy and when they got to a motel room and he handed her the money, I'd break in and pull out my phony police badge. The guy would run and I got to keep the money!" She laughed again. "If he didn't run, I shook him down for a thousand dollars or threatened to tell his wife and lock him up. One day this girl propositioned a cop. When they got to the motel room and I broke in and pulled out my badge, he pulled out his badge!" Terry fell on the cot, laughing.

I told Terry about my arrest and how Jesus had come into my life and totally changed me. She was silent throughout the story and when I had finished, she still didn't say anything.

"Terry, Jesus loves you," I said.

She looked at me with contempt. "Celeste, that's all right for the dummies in this place, but you can't sell that Jesus-loves-you bit to anyone with a brain!"

I let the subject drop.

When the others came in after 4 p.m. Terry sat on her cot until she realized we were having a Bible study. Then she left.

As the days passed I became fond of Terry. She was generally a very friendly, warm person. Occasionally, though, she would sit on her cot without speaking, without acknowledging my presence. "Is anything the matter?" I asked her one time.

"If there was, I wouldn't tell you," she said, "because you'd start that preaching."

On a Sunday afternoon, however, after she'd had a visit from her mother, she returned to the cell visibly shaken.

"Terry, what's the matter?" I asked.

"My mother had to quit her job because she's going blind."

"I'm sorry," I said. "Isn't there anyone else in the family to help her?"

"No," she said. "I was her main support. My father's dead. He worked as a bank guard and was killed in a shootout a couple of years ago."

No wonder she was so morose at times. As she went on talking, she never broke down, never shed a tear. "If I could stay out of jail, I could take care of my mother. I've been busted twelve times in the last seven years," she said.

"Terry, Jesus can turn your life around if you'll let Him."

"Don't start with that!" she said.

Of all the inmates I'd witnessed to in the past three months she was the most difficult to convince. As long as I kept off the subject of Jesus, Terry was my friend.

The next morning when I was leaving for my November court appearance, Terry was back in good spirits. "Celeste, if you go to trial today you don't have to worry," she said. "The judge will send you to a hospital. I never saw anyone who looked so worn out."

When I returned from court Terry asked, "Well, how did it go this time?"

"The D. A. got another adjournment. His witnesses fled the country." I laughed.

"Celeste, I don't understand you," she said. "I mean at your age and with your looks, you could be a movie star. When you finally go to trial and those girls take the stand against you, you'll get life and you're not even depressed!"

"Since I found Jesus, nothing can get me down," I said.

"You didn't find Jesus." Terry was trying to be patient with me. "There isn't any Jesus and there isn't any God. You found a philosophy. You psyched yourself."

"I know Jesus is real," I said, "because he lives in me."

"When I can understand God, then I'll believe," she said.

"God cannot be understood through the mind," I said. "He can only be understood through your spirit, your heart."

This was the longest Terry had listened to me talk about the Lord. "It takes faith," I added.

"That's a cop-out!" The anger was starting.

"You take other things on faith, Terry. You can't understand electricity, but you believe in it."

"Yeah, sure!"

"Terry, Jesus loves you so much that if you'd been the only one in the world, He would have gone to the cross for you."

"If he loves me so much, why did He let my father get killed? If He loves me so much, why is my mother going blind?"

For the first time I saw tears in Terry's eyes. "Terry, all the crimes, all the tragedies are the result of man's disobedience to God," I said.

"Yeah, sure! Tell me about it!"

I didn't say anything else, but I was happy to see that finally there was a chink in Terry's armor.

Several days later when I returned to my cell after work, I heard heart-rending cries coming from cell twelve. That was Jenny's cell, but it wasn't Jenny crying. And it was not the sick crying of a girl suffering withdrawal symptoms. It was grief. A few minutes later when the girls were in my cell for the Bible study, Jenny came in with a new inmate. "This is Janice," she said. "I told her you could help, Celeste."

Janice was very young, no more than twenty-one, and she appeared dazed.

"Sit down on my cot, Janice," I said.

She sat down, but she wouldn't look at anyone.

"Janice, you can tell us what happened," I said gently.

Immediately she began sobbing. After a couple of minutes she got control of herself and said, "I killed my mother."

There was a prolonged silence as everyone waited for her to continue.

"My mother and I were drinking very heavily," she said. "We're both alcoholics. I mean my mother *was* an alcoholic. We got into an argument and she picked up a kitchen knife and came after me. Then I picked up a knife and stabbed her. I didn't mean to kill her." She put her hands over her face and her body shook with sobs.

"Janice, God will forgive you," I said. Then I told her about my years of prostitution. "The Lord forgave me," I said, "and He'll forgive you."

"There can be no forgiveness for my sin," she said.

"There is only one unpardonable sin," I said. "and that is blasphemy against the Holy Ghost."

Her eyes widened.

"I'll prove it to you," I said.

I opened the Bible and found the scripture and read it to her: "Wherefore I say unto you, All manner of sin and blasphemy shall be forgiven unto men: but the blasphemy against the Holy Ghost shall not be forgiven unto men." (Matthew 12:31)

She was very still and her eyes never left my face.

"Janice, St. Paul massacred thousands of Christians in cold blood, but God forgave him for all those murders. And Paul went on to become the greatest apostle of them all!"

She regarded me with wonder.

"The Bible says 'If we confess our sins, he is faithful and just to forgive us our sins, and to cleanse us from all unrighteousness.'" (I John 1:9)

Immediately Janice got down on her knees and cried out, "Jesus, if You could forgive St. Paul for thousands of murders done in cold blood, You can forgive me!"

With those words her face became radiant and she cried out, "Thank you, Jesus!" over and over again.

Every girl in my cell was crying and praising the Lord.

An hour later, Janice left my cell a new girl. Because of the change in her, the next day four more inmates came to the Bible study and gave their hearts to Christ. After that Janice never missed a chance to witness about the transforming power of Jesus Christ.

A new inmate, Della, was brought to our tier. She was a Black Panther almost six feet tall and very muscular. The first time I saw her, her eyes burned right through me and I shuddered. She sat at our table in the mess hall and at every meal she made a point of staring at me. I pretended not to notice but then she would put her fork down and, ignoring the remarks and laughter directed at her, she would continue to stare at me. One morning I received a kite from Della. "Dear Celeste, You are one beautiful girl. Do you want to come to my cell or shall I go to yours? Della."

I continued to ignore her advances and one afternoon when I was alone, she stopped in front of my cell.

"What's your answer?" she asked.

"I am not interested," I said flatly.

"Oh, you're not!" she said. "Well, I am!"

"Don't come in here!" I shouted.

With that, she hurled a large, heavy jar of cold cream which hit me in the calf. I doubled over in pain, grabbing my leg. She lunged at me and punched me in the eye. I fell on the cot, screaming. Terry came running with some other inmates and Della left.

The next day I had a black eye and my entire leg had turned blue and was swelling. Mother Jones came by at four o'clock to take the head count. When she saw me she said, "Celeste, what happened to you?"

I told her and she said, "Well, honey, you have to see the doctor. That leg looks bad."

An hour later I was in the infirmary and Dr. Voytels was examining my leg. "Who assaulted you?" he asked.

"You don't expect me to give out her name, do you, Doctor?" I asked. I'd seen what happened to Margo after she'd ratted out a butch. She had been beaten by three butches and had to be hospitalized in Bellview for two weeks.

"Did you fight back?" the doctor asked.

"No," I said. "The Bible says to turn the other cheek."

"You'll have to stay in the infirmary until I'm satisfied you're all right," he said.

Dr. Voytels left the room and when he returned he said, "I've made an appointment for you to be seen by Dr. Eisenstat, our psychologist. He'll be in on Thursday."

A nurse brought me a hospital gown and I was put to bed. Later in the day my friend Jenny came to see me. She worked as an aide in the infirmary. "What did the doctor say?" she asked.

"He made an appointment for me to see the psychologist," I said. "He thinks I have some screws loose."

"Well, there are a lot of people in this joint who think you're crazy and can't stand you because of your love for Jesus," she said.

"The Bible says 'ye shall be hated of all men for my name's sake,'" I said. (Matthew 10:22)

"I've already found that out," Jenny said.

A few days later Dr. Eisenstat came in with my chart. "Celeste, do you like it here?" he asked.

"Yes, I do," I said.

"You like being in jail?"

"Yes, sir!"

"Why?" he asked.

"There are many inmates in here who are on their way to hell," I said. "And I want to lead them to salvation."

"When you were assaulted, why didn't you hit back?" he asked.

"I wouldn't be a good witness for Christ if I hit back," I

said.

"You can't let people beat up on you," he said. "Would you like to go home?"

"I'm not ready to go home," I said. "There are too many girls here who need Jesus."

"You have become institutionalized," he said. Then he wrote something in my chart, put it down and left the room.

Immediately I opened the chart and read what he had written—schizophrenic.

When he returned he said, "When you're discharged from the infirmary, you had better be prepared to fight back. You are a very attractive girl and you'll continue to be a prime target for aggresive lesbians."

A week later I was discharged from the infirmary. My leg was back to its normal size and my eye was clear. Despite the week of rest however, I was still tired.

When I got back to my cell Terry said, "Welcome back. This joint has been like a tomb since you were gone. But what's wrong with you? Why are you so exhausted?"

"Nothing's wrong," I said.

"I know what's wrong with you," she said. "With all your talk about how Jesus holds you above your problems, I think facing heavy time is finally getting to you."

Only when Terry became born again would she understand how I could be facing heavy time and yet have complete peace. "Believe me, Terry, I'm not upset about facing heavy time," I said. "I'm not upset about anything. Terry, when you accept Jesus you will no longer be bitter about your father's death. Jesus didn't promise to do away with problems, but He did promise to bring us through them. In the midst of heartache you can be happy!"

"There's no such thing as happiness," she said. "You don't have to look far to know that."

"I'm happy," I said.

"It won't last," she said.

"It lasted since April, seven months ago."

"Forget it," she said. "I don't want to talk about it."

The following morning I became alarmed when I spit up blood. I couldn't imagine what had caused it. Throughout the rest of the day and night I continued to cough and spit up blood. Before falling asleep that night I prayed. "Jesus, whatever it is," I said, "I know you can cure it." As the days went by I continued coughing and spitting up blood and in larger quantities. When Mother Jones came around on Friday afternoon to take the head count, I told her about it.

"I'll put your name on the list to see the doctor," she said.

Monday morning Mother Jones escorted me to the infirmary.

A nurse said, "Today you'll have lab work done and a chest x-ray taken. Then tomorrow morning the doctor will see you."

After x-rays were taken and as I was leaving the infirmary, I saw Jenny. "It's probably nothing," she said.

"I hope you're right," I said.

That night on her way to the Rec Room, Jenny stopped by my cell. "Celeste, I'm sorry you're so sick," she said.

"What do you mean, sick?"

"I heard the doctor say you have TB."

"Oh, my God!"

"Oh, don't say anything!" she cried. "I could lose my job. I was sure he had called you back."

Jenny left, following the other inmates to the Rec Room. When there was no one left on the tier but me, I got down on my knees. "Oh, Jesus!" I cried. "You wouldn't save me and then let me get TB!" I began to cry. "Lord, I don't want to go to a hospital and spend the rest of my life taking special care of myself."

When I had stopped crying I said, "Jesus, if You'll heal me of TB, I'll be your missionary for the rest of my life!" As soon as I'd spoken those words peace like I'd never experienced before saturated my being and I knew for a certainty that Jesus would heal me.

When Terry came back from the Rec Room I said, "Jenny heard the doctor say I have TB."

"Oh, no!" she cried.

"I'm not worried about it, Terry," I said, "because Jesus is going to heal me."

"Now that's going too far," she said. "Celeste, if you're healed of TB, I'll become a believer."

"Praise the Lord!" I said.

"The fact is," she said, "you'll be going to Bellview Hospital tomorrow and then you'll spend years in a sanitarium."

After the lights were out and Terry was asleep, I sat up in bed and began praising God. I must have been praising Him for almost an hour when my attention was drawn to the door of the cell. In the faint light from the corridor I could make out a very tall figure. As I looked, I saw sandals and the edge of a white robe. "Jesus!" I cried and as He vanished, a warmth went through my body and I knew that I was healed.

When I got up the next morning, for the first time in weeks I did not spit up blood. After breakfast Mother Jones came to my cell. "I have to take you to the infirmary again, Celeste," she said.

On the way over I repeated what Jenny had told me.

"The good Lord isn't going to let anything happen to you, honey," she said.

"Jesus already healed me!" I said.

"I hope so, honey," she said. "I sure do hope so."

In the infirmary I had another set of x-rays taken. Then the nurse told me to go into the examining room and a few minutes later Dr. Voytels came in, frowning. "Celeste, we'll have to have another set of x-rays to be sure."

I smiled. I knew what had happened. Following the nurse to the x-ray room, I had a third set taken. Several minutes later the doctor saw me again. "I don't understand it," he said. "Yesterday, Celeste, the x-rays showed an active case of tuberculosis, but now it seems to be arrested."

"Praise the Lord!" I shouted.

Mother Jones and Jenny heard me and both of them began to cry with joy.

"Come on, Mother Jones," I said. "I have a friend who's about to become a believer!"

We laughed all the way down in the elevator and through the corridor. When I reached my cell, Terry was lying on her cot, reading a mystery novel. She looked up. "When do you go to Bellview?" she asked.

"I don't have to go to the hospital, Terry," I said. "The doctor says he doesn't understand it, but the TB has been arrested!"

Terry stared at me dumbfounded, then she began crying softly. "Oh, God, forgive me for not believing!" she cried.

When Terry asked Jesus into her heart, her countenance was transformed. "Celeste, I'm so happy!" she said. "I've never been this happy in my whole life!"

When we went to the mess hall for lunch, Terry immediately began witnessing to the inmates at our table.

"Another nut!" one inmate said.

"Two of a kind!" another one said.

Half the women at our table were laughing at Terry, but no amount of ridicule, no amount of laughter could stop her. She was on fire for Jesus and nothing was going to shut her up. Terry became immersed in the Bible and couldn't get enough of it.

"I didn't know what I was getting into," she said. "I was a big mouth for the devil, and now I'm going to be a big mouth for the Lord!"

I was due to be released from the Women's House of Detention a few days before Christmas.

"Terry, when I leave, you are going to take over the Bible study," I said.

"I'd love to," she said. "I don't know the scriptures half

as well as you do, but leading a Bible study is my kind of thing!"

"The Holy Ghost is the best teacher. He'll enlighten and quicken the scriptures to your heart," I said.

"What are you going to do when you're out of here, Celeste?"

"I plan to enroll in a Bible school as soon as possible," I said.

"That will be terrific!" she said.

The morning I was released, Mother Jones came into my cell and put her arms around me. "Celeste, your mother is waiting for you downstairs!" she said. There were tears in her eyes. "I am going to miss you, honey, but I'm glad you're getting out. You're too good for this place."

A crowd of inmates had gathered near my cell. The girls were crying and kissing me good bye. Janice came up to me. "Oh, Celeste, what would have become of me if I hadn't met you?"

I put my arm around her. "Now you can bring Jesus to those in despair," I said.

As I got in the elevator and went down to the lobby, I spoke to the Lord. "Jesus, now I know where you want me. My mission field is in the prison. You want me to minister to inmates."

Doing heavy time wasn't going to be so bad after all!

Chapter XXV

The Second Trial

When I got home, one of the first things I did was try to locate Melanie. She'd promised to write to me, but I hadn't heard from her since the day she was released from prison last August. Christmas was only three days away and I wanted to have her over for the holidays. I kept calling Tracy's apartment until finally I reached her. "Tracy, do you know where I can find Melanie?" I asked.

"I don't know where she is, Celeste. She hasn't been able to work in any of the houses because her habit got so bad they wouldn't let her in."

"What?" I cried. "Melanie kicked her habit in prison!"

"Well, she got right back on the stuff the day she got out," Tracy said.

"I can't believe it!"

"She's much worse now," Tracy said. "She's shooting three times what she used to shoot. She's hit the streets."

"Oh, no!" I cried.

I hung up and called a couple of johns who might know where I could locate Melanie. When I reached Fred Bently and asked about her, he said, "Melanie's in bad shape." Then he gave me the name and address of a bar in China-town. "That's where you'll find Melanie most nights," he

said.

The night before Christmas Eve I drove to Chinatown. At 10:30 I walked into the bar and took a table in the corner farthest away from the door. From where I was sitting I could see everyone who came in and I was prepared to wait all night if necessary to find Melanie. It was a cheap, run-down place and the people were shabby and loud. Melanie must be in really bad shape to come in here, I thought. As I glanced around the dimly lighted room I was sickened. The smell of alcohol and the clouds of cigarette smoke oppressed me. The sudden bursts of laughter grated on my nerves. It was hard to believe that not too long ago this had been a way of life for me.

When the barmaid came over and I ordered a coke, she said, "Would you like a straw to go with it?"

I overlooked her sarcasm and when she returned with the coke, I tipped her two dollars. After that she didn't make any more cracks when I ordered a soft drink.

I kept looking at my watch, hoping Melanie would come in. It was after midnight when a petite young girl walked in. From the outline of her figure, it looked like Melanie. She took a seat at the bar and as I watched, I saw that she did not have thick glossy dark hair. Still, there was something familiar about her. I got up and started toward the bar. Now I could see her face in profile—the finely chiseled features, the flawless complexion. It was Melanie, all right. Then I stood directly behind her and saw that she had very little hair and there was a large bald spot at the back of her head. Suddenly she turned and stared unbelievingly into my eyes. "Celeste!" she cried.

"Oh, Melanie!" I took her by the arm. "Let's get out of here," I said.

When we were outside she put her arms around me and hung on like a child. Then standing back she said, "Oh, Celeste, I've thought of you so often!"

My heart froze. Her teeth were black and rotted away.

Tears rushed to my eyes. I'd seen other junkies who looked like this, but this wasn't just another junkie. This was Melanie.

"You can see what's become of me," she said.

"Thank God I found you!" I said. "You are coming home with me right now. I'm getting you off that stuff and..."

She wouldn't let me finish. "Celeste, it's too late. It's no use."

"Melanie, listen to me. There's still hope."

"I've been hustling the streets for $5 a trick," she said. "I have twenty to thirty guys a night."

The tears were running down my cheeks. "Melanie, I won't leave you here."

"Celeste, I feel that eventually I am going to kill myself."

"It doesn't have to end like this," I said. "Jesus can turn your life around!"

"Good bye, Celeste," she said and started walking down the street.

"Melanie!" I cried, but I knew she wouldn't come back. I stood there watching her frail form disappear until she became lost in the night.

A few weeks later I enrolled in a Bible school, a beautiful place on acres of wooded countryside.

"Everyone in the school has been following your case, Celeste," Mrs. Briggs, the dean, said. "We heard you'd been saved and that you were preaching the gospel in the prison."

"It was the most glorious experience of my life, bringing inmates into the kingdom of God!" I said.

"Celeste, you have a tremendous testimony and I know you'll be a blessing to our school," she said.

I was accepted and loved by the students. I was learning that when you meet born again believers, the love is immediate and real and lasting. I enjoyed the Bible courses the most and it never ceased to amaze me that no matter how often I read a passage of scripture, I could always find new meaning. The Bible was the only book that could be read over and over again and still be exciting, still speak to my heart.

Once in a while I became overwhelmed with guilt and remorse for my past life, but the scripture Mrs. Daly had given me always restored peace in my heart: "I, even I, am he that blotteth out thy transgressions for mine own sake, and will not remember thy sins."

I'd been in the school several weeks when we studied about the baptism of the Holy Ghost. Many of the students had received the baptism. A few of them prophesied during Chapel services and this reminded me of the times I'd gone to the little Pentecostal church. I could never forget the times Grandma was filled with the spirit, tears rolling down her cheeks. Her words came back to me: "That's where I get my strength, Celeste. You can't make it as a Christian without the baptism of the Holy Ghost."

One night before falling asleep as I prayed I said, "Jesus, please baptize me with the Holy Ghost."

A few days later I awoke at 5:30, one hour before we had to get up. I felt impelled to go to the chapel immediately instead of waiting until the seven o'clock service. I dressed quickly and within minutes I was alone in the chapel. I began to praise the Lord. Suddenly a scripture came to mind: "John answered saying unto them all, I indeed baptize you with water; but one mightier than I cometh, the latchet of whose shoes I am not worthy to unloose: he shall baptize you with the Holy Ghost and with fire." (Luke 3:16)

"Oh, Jesus!" I cried, "if You will baptize me with the Holy Ghost, I'll not only give you my heart, I'll give you my life!"

As soon as I'd uttered those words, a warmth went through my body and like a feather I fell to the floor, slain under the power of God. Then without effort, without thought, strange sounds began to pour forth from my lips.

I was praying in tongues! Love bubbled up in my spirit and I became overwhelmed with joy! I went on communicating with God in a heavenly language only He understood. When I stood and looked around, I had no idea how long I'd been on the floor praying. It seemed like only minutes; but as I saw students coming for the service, I realized I'd been there for over an hour.

After that, I understood what Grandma had meant when she said that was where she got her strength. Each night as I prayed, I found myself slipping into tongues without even being aware of it. When praying in this new language, I could bring down the power of God and always I was refreshed and renewed by this closest of all contacts with Him.

The last weekend of February I was home for my monthly visit and Mother was depressed. "Grandma has been failing," she said.

"I'll visit her first thing tomorrow morning," I said.

Saturday morning before we'd finished our breakfast the telephone rang. I answered it. It was Aunt Connie. "Come quickly," she said, "Grandma is going fast."

"Oh, no!" I cried. "We'll be right over!"

Mother had already jumped to her feet and was putting on her coat.

"I'll get Grandpa," I said, grabbing my coat.

I ran out the door and across the street. Grandpa was shoveling snow off the sidewalk and when he saw me running toward him, he turned ashen. "It's Grandma," he said.

"Yes, Grandpa," I said, "get in my car."

Mother was already in the car when we got in. It was only two blocks to Aunt Connie's house. When we walked into Grandma's room, Aunt Connie was standing over the bed crying. Grandma's eyes were closed and there was a smile on her face. Mother began crying and Grandpa fell to his knees next to the bed. "Lorda, I'ma sorry!" he cried out. "Forgivea my sinsa anda comea into mya hearta!"

I picked up Grandma's Bible and knelt next to Grandpa.

I placed the Bible on her head and prayed. "Oh, Father, nothing is impossible with You," I said. "If it be Your will, I rebuke this spirit of death in Grandma. In the name of Jesus, I command Grandma to rise!"

Immediately my body went backward and I fell lightly against the wall, the way I'd been slain in the Spirit in the chapel. Then an inaudible but distinct voice said, "Fear not, my child. Death is a victory and a reward for my children. She has earned her reward. Go and do thou likewise!"

After Grandma's death, Mother told me Grandpa was a changed man. He stopped drinking. He was no longer angry with the world, but gentle and loving and filled with remorse for the way he'd treated Grandma all those years.

"He spends hours in his rocking chair just talking to the Lord," Mother said.

"Grandma always said he would be saved when she died," I said.

Meanwhile at the Bible school I continued to make progress in my studies. The deeper I was into the Word of God, the stronger and more joyful I became. I was learning how God speaks to His children on a one-to-one basis through His Holy Word.

Through the winter and spring I went to court every month and each time it proved to be an exercise in futility. After the April court appearance I said to Mr. Rosenthal, "It's ridiculous that after fourteen months they still haven't brought my case to trial!"

"It's a waste of the tax payer's money, dragging it out like this," he said, "but some day it will come to an end."

One April morning I was summoned to Mrs. Briggs' office. As I walked in, her eyes filled with compassion.

"What's wrong?" I asked.

"Someone you know, Celeste..." she said, handing me a newspaper and pointing to a headline. *Vice Jill Dead from Overdose*. I knew right away it was Melanie. Quickly I read through the account. Melanie had been found dead in a furnished room in Chinatown. The article identified her as "one of the top call girls arrested in the raid of the notorious prostitution ring broken February 14." There was no doubt it was suicide, police said, because she had left a note.

I ran to my room, sobbing. I couldn't believe that Melanie had taken her own life. And yet I'd known even before she'd said it that night, that it would end like this. Melanie, my best friend, so sweet, so beautiful. Oh, if only she had come to Jesus!

In the days and weeks that followed Melanie's suicide, every time I started to break down, I prayed in tongues and within seconds Jesus lifted me above the grief. That was truly a miracle, every bit as great as being healed of TB.

In May I was asked to sing in the choir at the graduation exercises. We practiced daily for two weeks and on the night of graduation the auditorium was packed with parents and friends. Early in the program the choir walked onto the stage. As the pianist struck the first chord, a man came running down the center aisle with a camera slung over his shoulder. I recognized him as one of the photographers who had followed me around at every court appearance. "Come on, Celeste!" he shouted. "Let's have a picture of you with a Bible in your hand!"

I ran off the stage and out of the building. I got in my car and drove home and never returned to the school again. I didn't want to bring reproach upon the school.

I spent the summer at home. Life was quiet and uneventful until Mr. Rosenthal called in mid-August. "Celeste, we have to be in court Monday," he said. "And this time I have it on good authority the judge is going to insist the case be concluded."

"That's hard to believe after all this time," I said.

"When Judge Fineburg runs out of patience, that's it!" Rosenthal said.

Sunday Mother carried on all day. "If the case does go to trial," she said, "I'll never see you again except behind prison bars!"

"Mother, don't you realize that no matter what my life is like in prison, Jesus will be with me? I'm glad I was caught. I'm glad I was busted. If I hadn't been, I never would have come back to Jesus."

But there was no consoling her.

Monday morning as Rita's car pulled up in front of the house, Mother wrapped her arms around me and began sobbing. There was nothing to do but pull away from her and run out the door.

"There's no way to comfort her," I said.

"I know," Rita said.

Rita hardly spoke on the ride to Manhattan. At Mr. Rosenthal's office, once again he went over the legal points and schooled me in my responses. There was an urgency in his manner. "This is it, Celeste," he said, looking at me with compassion.

"I'll be all right, really," I said.

Rita and I followed him to the Supreme Court. When Rita parked the car, suddenly she began crying. "I'm sorry, Celeste," she said. "I just can't help it."

"Rita, I've been prepared for this for a long time," I said. "I don't want to spend the rest of my life in prison, but with Jesus I can do it. I can do it and be happy."

"That's my only consolation," she said.

Minutes later I was seated at the witness table with Mr. Rosenthal.

After court was called to order, Judge Fineburg turned to the assistant district attorney, Mr. O'Rourke. "Are you prepared to prosecute the defendant?" he asked.

"Your honor," Mr. O'Rourke said, "my witnesses have not shown up. I would like an adjournment."

"Another adjournment?" The judge's voice was raised. "Mr. O'Rourke, do you realize this case has been pending for eighteen months?"

Mr. O'Rourke's neck was turning red. "Yes, your honor," he said.

"This court is in session," the judge said. "Let's bring this case to trial right now. Surely, by this time you must have some witnesses. Where are they, Mr. O'Rourke?"

"Your honor, a couple of witnesses have died. A few have fled the country. Some are in prison. Others have relocated and can't be found..."

"This case has got to be concluded!"

I'd never heard the judge use this tone before.

"Your honor," Mr. O'Rourke said, "I respectfully request one more adjournment. I believe I can locate a couple of witnesses."

"No more adjournments!" the judge shouted.

"Then all we can offer the defendant is a misdemeanor plea," Mr. O'Rourke said quietly.

"A misdemeanor plea!" the judge roared. "This woman had been indicted on twenty-seven felonies and ten misdemeanors and all you can offer her is one misdemeanor plea?"

A murmur went through the courtroom and Judge Fineburg banged his gavel. "I will not tolerate one outburst in this courtroom!" he shouted.

Mr. O'Rourke stood there with his head down.

"Do you mean to tell me, Mr. O'Rourke, that after all the people who signed statements against this woman, that now there is not one who will testify against her?"

"That is correct, your honor," he said.

"Mr. O'Rourke," the judge's voice was suddenly quiet. "Your handling of this case has been most negligent. In eighteen months you have not been able to come up with a single witness to achieve a conviction!" The judge called Mr. Rosenthal to the bench and spoke in a lowered tone. Rosenthal returned to the witness table.

"Accept the misdemeanor plea," he said to me. "You'll

get from one to three years."

"Will the defendant please stand?" the judge asked.

I was numb with shock at the turn of events. I stood up.

"Young lady," the judge said, "you are very fortunate that this court has been unable to obtain a conviction against you. Are you willing to accept this misdemeanor plea?"

"Yes, your honor," I said.

Judge Fineburg banged his gavel. "Sentencing to be on September 14 at 9:30. Bail continued."

The courtroom erupted into pandemonium. Mr. Rosenthal was shaking my hand. Flash bulbs were popping and a reporter shouted, "Celeste, how does it feel to be facing a couple of years after you thought you'd be doing heavy time?"

Rita was hugging me. "Wait 'till Mother hears this!" she cried.

And as I started to walk out of the courtroom, that inaudible but unmistakable voice said, "Woman, where are thine accusers?"

Tears rushed to my eyes and I said, "There are none, Lord!"

Epilog

Celeste Clemente was sentenced to an indefinite term (one to three years) at Bedford Hills Correctional Facility in New York.

For the past fifteen years she has been bringing the gospel of salvation to prison and jails in major cities throughout the United States. In December 1983 Celeste returned to Bedford Hills Correctional Facility, where she was incarcerated, giving her testimony and preaching the message of salvation. Many girls accepted Jesus Christ as their personal Saviour. Many inmates have been saved through reading this book.

Now as an evangelist known as Sr. Celeste, she conducts, revivals throughout the country. She has a ministry in Fort Worth and Houston, Texas, Miami, Florida, and Atlanta, Georgia. Her home base is in New York, where the Lord has given her one of the largest street ministries. Sr. Celeste has appeared on the 700 Club, PTL, 100 Huntley Street, and many other Christian networks, witnessing the delivering power of Jesus Christ and His faithfulness to answer a simple grandmother's prayer.

She is available for revivals and speaking engagements throughout the country.

*Interested parties may contact: *Sr. Celeste Ministries*
P.O. Box 114
Islip, N.Y. 11751
516-277-6374

*For additional copies of this book send check or money order of $7.00 to the address above.

Evangelist Sr. Celeste